Exam

Mathematics

Michael Jennings

Contents

Examination boards

AQA Assessment and Qualifications Alliance
Devas Street,
Manchester,
M15 6EX
www.aqa.org.uk

EDEXCEL
Stewart House,
32 Russell Square,
London,
WC1B 5DN
www.edexcel.org.uk

OCR Oxford Cambridge and RSA Examinations
1 Hills Road,
Cambridge,
CB1 2EU
www.ocr.org.uk

CCEA Northern Ireland Council for Curriculum, Examinations and Assessment
29 Clarendon Road,
Belfast,
BT1 3BG
www.ccea.org.uk

WJEC Welsh Joint Education Committee
245 Western Avenue,
Cardiff,
CF5 2YX
www.wjec.co.uk

This book is based on a new specification for A level Mathematics which will be taught in schools and colleges from September 2004 for first examination in June 2005. All five examination boards (**Edexcel, AQA, OCR, CCEA,** and **WJEC**) have produced their own specification but the general structure of all of these specifications is broadly the same.

To obtain an A level qualification in Mathematics, candidates must study:

Four (Pure) Core units, C1, C2, C3 and C4 plus two Applied units.

The Applied unit could be in Mechanics (M1), Statistics (S1) or in Decision or Discrete Mathematics (D1).

Candidates are not permitted the use of a calculator in the C1 unit but can use a calculator (scientific or graphical) in the other units.

Each unit will be assessed via a one and half hour written paper.

There is no coursework, except for AQA, who have coursework versions of their Applied units.

N.B. The above is a general outline and there are one or two exceptions/variations.

More detail on each of the new A level mathematics specifications is available at the appropriate website:

www.edexcel.org.uk   www.aqa.org.uk
www.ocr.org.uk   www.ccea.org.uk
www.wjec.org.uk

A2 exams

Different types of questions

Questions on mathematics papers have varying degrees of structure to them. Those at the beginning of a paper tend to be short and sharp and worth only a few marks and thus there is little opportunity to break the question down into smaller parts. However, as you progress through the paper, the questions become longer and more challenging and will often have several parts to them. These parts could be totally independent or there may be a common theme running through a question where the examiner is attempting to lead you through the early parts in order to give you a hint on a method that might be used to do a later, more difficult part – the wording "hence, or otherwise" is an indication of this type of question.

A question can also be broken down into smaller parts in order for a candidate who gets stuck on an early part to, nonetheless, be able to go on and score marks on later parts. To this end, the answer may be given in a particular part and the candidates be asked to show it. Thus, if a candidate is unable to derive the correct result, he or she can use the printed answer to hopefully progress further through the question.

Sometimes candidates may be required, as the first part of a question, to produce a proof or derivation of a standard result or formula which is then used in a subsequent part or parts to solve a particular problem. Explanations or definitions of particular terms may also be asked for, particularly on statistics papers.

You may also be asked to comment on or interpret a result (in statistics or decision mathematics), explain a modelling assumption and where it is used (in mechanics), identify a flaw in an argument (in core mathematics) or how a particular model could be refined to make it more realistic.

What examiners look for

- clear and concise methods, although any valid method, no matter how long, will be given full credit.
- appropriate and accurate use of notation and symbolism.
- large and clearly labelled diagrams and graphs where appropriate.
- appropriate and accurate use of technology (e.g. a calculator).
- the ability to interpret and comment on results obtained.

What makes an A, C and E grade candidate?

- **A grade candidates** have a broad knowledge of mathematics and can apply that knowledge in a wide variety of situations, including unfamiliar scenarios, accurately and efficiently. They are strong on all of the units. The minimum mark for a grade A is 80% on the Uniform Mark Scale.
- **C grade candidates** have a fair knowledge of mathematics but find it less easy to apply their knowledge in unfamiliar situations. Their work is less accurate and they have weaknesses on some of the units. The minimum mark for a grade C is 60% on the Uniform Mark Scale.
- **E grade candidates** have a poor knowledge of mathematics and are unable to apply it in unfamiliar situations. Their work has many errors and they are unable to recall key facts and techniques. The minimum mark for a grade E is 40% on the Uniform Mark Scale.

Successful revision

Revision skills

- By far the best way to revise for mathematics is by doing mathematics i.e. by solving problems. Of course you have to learn the theory but unless you can apply the theory to actually tackle problems, the knowledge is of little use. It is therefore essential, if your preparation is to be effective, that you encounter as many different situations and scenarios as possible, by doing as many practice questions as possible, so that you can learn how to recognise which techniques will be appropriate to solve a particular type of problem and which will not.

- When revising the theory, try to summarise, as concisely as possible, the key points and how they relate to other parts of the specification. Writing out your own concise notes (the briefer the better) for each specification topic can be a good way of learning material.

Practice questions

To use this book effectively

- Examine the grade A and grade C sample answers and make sure that you understand where the errors have been made and how to correct them.

- Try the exam practice questions – don't be tempted to look at the answers too quickly if you get stuck; you will learn a great deal more from a question if you struggle with it and eventually sort it out or at least make some progress, by yourself, using worked examples in your notes or in a textbook to guide you.

- When you feel confident and ready, try the mock exam papers.

Common errors

Many errors occur due to careless work with signs, particularly when removing brackets, and errors in basic algebra and trigonometry.

1. **Many of the most common errors occur as a result of students treating all functions, f, as being linear**
   i.e. $f(a + b) = f(a) + f(b)$,   for all a and b.

   e.g. $(a + b)^2 = a^2 + b^2$, or similar

   $$\sqrt{(a + b)} = \sqrt{a} + \sqrt{b}$$

   $$\frac{1}{a + b} = \frac{1}{a} + \frac{2}{b}$$

   $$\sin(A + B) = \sin A + \sin B$$

   $$\ln(A + B) = \ln A + \ln B$$

   $$e^{x + y} = e^x + e^y$$

   Of course none of the above are true, **in general** (some of them may be true in certain special cases). See if you can, where possible, correct them.

2. **Confusion with notation**
   e.g.
   f^{-1}, the **inverse** of f, is often confused with f', the **derivative** of f
   fg means "do g first then f", not the other way round.

How to boost your grade

- Ensure that you do exactly as the question says, e.g. if you are told to use a particular method then you will receive no credit whatsoever for using a different method, even if you get the question right.

- Ensure that you give answers to the correct degree of accuracy when requested to do so – you will definitely lose marks if you don't.

- Show your working – a very high proportion of the available marks at A2 level are Method Marks.

- You can answer the questions in any order that you like – you should attempt a few of the shorter questions at the beginning of the paper to boost your confidence, making sure that you leave yourself plenty of time for the last two or three questions, for which there are a very high number of marks.

- For the shorter questions, make life easier for the examiner, by ruling off at the end of a question and either leave a space before you start the next question, or if you are near the bottom of the page, start on a fresh piece of paper. Always start the longer questions on a fresh page. This will help to avoid copying and transcription errors which are made when turning over a page.

- If you attempt a question using two different methods, then do not cross out either of them but instead leave both – the examiner will mark both and award you the better mark.

- Dimensional analysis, particularly in algebraic Mechanics questions, will often help to spot silly mistakes. For example, if you are asked to find the loss in kinetic energy in a particular problem and you obtain an answer of $5\,mu$, you should realise that you have made an error as this expression has momentum (or impulse) units.

- Don't work too quickly – try to check each line of working before moving on to the next – but on the other hand don't waste time e.g. by underlining everything; use your time sensibly – try to match the time that you use to the marks available for that question – if you get stuck on a question, particularly a short one, don't panic! Leave a space and go back to it later, if you have time.

- Familiarise yourself with the Formulae Booklet before you do the exam – make sure that you know what is in there and where it is situated.

- Make sure that you have a calculator with you when permitted (you are not allowed calculators for certain core units), and that it works!

- Put all your past papers together and look through them so that you are familiar with the type of questions that are asked and look through your copy of the specification to make sure that you have revised all the topics.

Glossary of terms used in examination questions

Prove – Show that a result is true, using a reasoned argument which starts from accepted basic results (the question will sometimes clarify what you can assume).

Write down, state – no justification is needed for your answer.

Calculate, find, determine, show, solve – show sufficient working to make your method clear.
(N.B. Answers without working will gain no credit).

Deduce, hence – use the given result or previous part to establish the result.

Sketch – graph paper not needed; show the general shape of a graph, where it crosses the axes (if it does), any asymptotes and any points of particular significance.

Draw – plot accurately on graph paper using a suitable scale.

Find the exact value – leave your answer as a fraction or in surds, or in terms of logarithms, exponentials or π; note that using a calculator is likely to introduce decimal approximations, resulting in a loss of marks.

Questions with model answers

C grade candidate – mark scored 7/12

Examiner's Commentary

(1) The temperature, $\theta\,°C$, of a cooling body after t minutes is given by

$$\theta = 10 + 20e^{-\frac{1}{2}t}, \; t \geq 0$$

(a) Find the temperature of the body when it started to cool. **[1]**

When $t = 0$, $\theta = 10 + 20e^0 = 30$ ←

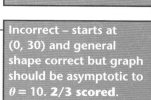

For help see *Revise A2 Study Guide* section 1

All correct, **1/1 scored.**

(b) Find the time taken for the body to cool to a temperature of 15 °C. **[4]**

$$15 = 10 + 20e^{-\frac{1}{2}t}$$ ←
$$5 = 20e^{-\frac{1}{2}t}$$
$$0.25 = e^{-\frac{1}{2}t}$$ ←
$$\ln 0.25 = \frac{1}{2}t$$ ←
$$2\ln 0.25 = t$$ ←

Correct start.

Correct method – isolating the e term.

Incorrect – candidate has lost the − sign.

Incorrect answer (that is in fact a negative time), **2/4 scored.**

(c) Sketch graph of θ against t. **[3]**

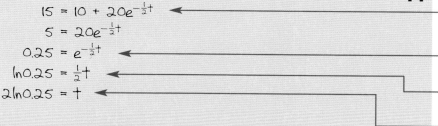

Incorrect – starts at (0, 30) and general shape correct but graph should be asymptotic to $\theta = 10$. **2/3 scored.**

(d) Find the rate at which the temperature of the body is falling when it starts to cool. **[4]**

$$\frac{d\theta}{dt} = -40e^{-\frac{1}{2}t}$$ ←

$$t = 0, \; \frac{d\theta}{dt} = -40$$ ←

Correct idea to differentiate but the candidate has in fact integrated.

Again correct idea but incorrect answer. **2/4 scored.**

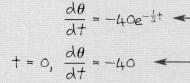

GRADE BOOSTER The ability to differentiate and integrate exponential functions correctly is crucial.

Core 3

(2) The functions f, g are defined by

$$f : x \to 6x - 1, x \in \mathbb{R}$$
$$g : x \to \frac{4}{x - 1}, x \in \mathbb{R}, x \neq 1.$$

(a) Find, in its simplest form, g^{-1}. **[4]**

$$\text{Let } y = \frac{4}{x - 1}$$

$$y(x - 1) = 4$$

$$yx - y = 4$$

$$yx = 4 + y$$

$$x = \frac{4}{y} + 1$$

$$\text{so, } g^{-1} : x \to \frac{4}{x} + 1$$

The correct start – let $y = g(x)$ as this is equivalent to $g^{-1}(y) = x$ (or put $x = g(y)$, equivalent to $g^{-1}(x) = y$, and make y the subject).

Clearing the fractions.

Making x the subject – the RHS is now $g^{-1}(y)$, from above.

This is a correct definition but the domain, $x \in \mathbb{R}, x \neq 0$, has been omitted – a common error, losing a mark, **3/4 scored**.

(b) State the range of g. **[1]**

$$y \geqslant 4.$$

Incorrect; generally it is much easier to find a domain; the range of g is the same as the domain of g^{-1} so the correct answer is $y \in \mathbb{R}, y \neq 0$, from part **(a)**. Note also that range of g^{-1} is same as domain of g, **0 scored**.

(c) Find, in its simplest form, $gf(x)$. **[2]**

$$gf(x) = g\{f(x)\}$$

$$= \frac{4}{f(x) - 1}$$

$$= \frac{4}{6x - 2}$$

$$= \frac{2}{3x - 1}$$

Putting this step in makes it obvious that gf means 'f then g'.

All correct, **2/2 scored**.

(d) Find the values of x for which $g(x) = f(x)$. **[5]**

$$\frac{4}{x - 1} = 6x - 1 \to 4 = (6x - 1)(x - 1)$$

$$\to 0 = 6x^2 - 7x - 3$$

$$\to 0 = (3x + 1)(2x - 3)$$

$$\to x = -\frac{1}{3} \text{ or } \frac{3}{2}$$

Clearing the fractions.

Multiplying out and collecting all the terms on one side.

Refactorising.

All correct, **5/5 scored**.

?

For help see Revise A2 Study Guide section 1

Exam practice questions

1.1 Algebra and functions

1 Solve the equation $\dfrac{1}{x^2 - 4} + \dfrac{3}{x + 2} = \dfrac{4}{5}$ [9]

2 **(a)** Sketch on the same axes the graphs of $y = |x|$ and $y = 2|x - 1|$. [2]

   (b) Solve the equation $|x| = 2|x - 1|$. [5]

3 Sketch, on different axes, the graphs of

   (a) $y = |\sin x|$, for $0° \leqslant x \leqslant 360°$ [2]

   (b) $y = \sin|x|$, for $-360° \leqslant x \leqslant 360°$ [2]

   (c) $y = \sin 2x$, for $0° \leqslant x \leqslant 360°$. [2]

4 Prove that the equation $\dfrac{2x + 3}{x - 1} + \dfrac{3x - 4}{x + 1} = 3$ has no real solutions. [7]

5 Express $\dfrac{7x - 15}{2(x - 2)(x - 1)} - \dfrac{7}{2x}$

   as a single algebraic fraction in its lowest terms. [5]

6 The function g is given by

   $g: x \to 2 - \dfrac{1}{x + 1}, x \in \mathbb{R}, x \neq -1.$

   (a) Find g^{-1}. [3]

   (b) State the range of g. [1]

   (c) Sketch the graph of $y = g(x)$. [4]

1.2 Trigonometry

1 Prove the following identities.

   (a) $\left(\dfrac{1 + \cos\theta}{\sin\theta}\right)^2 + \left(\dfrac{1 - \cos\theta}{\sin\theta}\right)^2 = 4\operatorname{cosec}^2\theta - 2.$ [6]

   (b) $(\operatorname{cosec} x + \cot x)(\sec x + \tan x) = (1 + \operatorname{cosec} x)(1 + \sec x).$ [5]

2 **(a)** Express $12\sin\theta + 5\cos\theta$ in the form $R\sin(\theta + \alpha)$,
       where $R > 0$ and $0° < \alpha < 90°$. [7]

   (b) Find the maximum and minimum values of $(12\sin\theta + 5\cos\theta)^3$, stating the values of
       θ at which they occur. [3]

   (c) Solve, for $0° < \theta < 360°$,

       $12\tan\theta + 5 = 4\sec\theta.$ [6]

3 **(a)** Given that $\sec A + \tan A = 2\cos A$,

show that $2\sin^2 A + \sin A - 1 = 0$. [4]

(b) Hence find the values of x, where $0 \leq x \leq 2\pi$, for which

$$\sec 2x + \tan 2x = 2\cos 2x,$$

giving your answers in terms of π. [6]

4 **(a)** Solve, for $0 \leq x < 360°$, the equation

$$2\cos(x + 50°) = \sin(x + 40°)$$

giving your answers to 1 decimal place. [6]

(b) Solve, $0 \leq x < 2\pi$, the equation $\cos 2x = 2\sin^2 x$

giving your answers in terms of π. [5]

1.3 Exponentials and logarithms

1 The points with coordinates (3, 0) and (4, 1) lie on the curve with equation

$$y = \log_{10}(px + q).$$

Find the values of p and q. [4]

2 A curve C has equation $y = 12 - e^{2x}$.

The point P has coordinates $(p, -4)$ and the point Q has coordinates $(\ln 2, q)$.

Given that both P and Q lie on C,

(a) find the values of p and q. [5]

(b) Find the coordinates of the point where C crosses the x-axis. [3]

(c) Find an equation for the tangent to C at P. [4]

3 Solve, to 2 decimal places,

(a) $e^{(2x+1)} = 10$, [4]

(b) $\ln(9 - 2x) = 2$. [4]

4 Solve the simultaneous equations

$$3x - \ln y - 6 = 0$$
$$x + \ln y^2 - 8 = 0.$$ [5]

5 A cup of tea is heated to 70 °C and then allowed to cool.

The temperature, θ °C, of the tea t minutes after it begins to cool is given by

$$\theta = 20 + Ae^{-kt}.$$

(a) Find the value of A. [2]

Given that $\theta = 45$ when $t = 4$,

(b) find, to 3 decimal places, the value of k, [4]

Answers on pages 13–22 Answers on pages 13–22 Answers on pages 13–22

1.4 Differentiation

1 (a) Sketch the curve with equation $y = 2e^x - 1$. [2]

(b) Find an equation of the normal to the curve at the point where $x = 0$. [7]

2 (a) Sketch the curve with equation $y = \ln x$. [1]

(b) Show that the equation
$$x + \ln x - 2 = 0$$
has one real root, α, and that $1.5 < \alpha < 2$. [4]

3 (a) Show graphically that the equation $x^3 - 8e^{-x} = 0$ has one real root, α. [4]

(b) Find the integer n such that $n < \alpha < n + 1$. [4]

(c) Use the iteration formula
$$x_{n+1} = (8e^{-x_n})^{\frac{1}{3}}, \ x_1 = 2$$
to find α correct to 1 decimal place. [4]

(d) Prove that your answer is the value of α to 1 decimal place. [3]

4 The number of bacteria, N, present in a sample, t hours after noon on a particular day, is given by
$$N = 2000e^{kt}, \text{ where } k \text{ is a constant.}$$
When $t = 0$, the rate of increase of the number of bacteria is 200 per hour.

(a) Find the value of k. [4]

(b) Find the number of bacteria present at 6 pm on the same day. [2]

5 Differentiate with respect to x

(a) $\ln(2x^2)$ [2]

(b) $x^2 \cos 4x$ [2]

(c) $4\sin^3(2x)$. [2]

6 The curve, C, has equation $y = \dfrac{2x}{1 + x^2}$.

(a) Show that $\dfrac{dy}{dx} = \dfrac{2(1 - x^2)}{(1 + x^2)^2}$. [3]

(b) Hence find the coordinates of the stationary points and distinguish between them. [6]

(c) Sketch the curve. [3]

Answers on pages 13–22 **Answers** on pages 13–22 **Answers** on pages 13–22

Core 3

1.5   Numerical methods

1 $f(x) = x^3 + x - 6\ln 2x$

where $x \in R$ and $x > 0$.

The curve C has equation $y = f(x)$. Given that C has a stationary point at $x = \alpha$

(a) show that $1 < \alpha < 2$.   [5]

(b) Using an iteration formula of the form
$$x_{n+1} = \sqrt[3]{p + qx_n}$$
where p and q are constants to be found, and with $x_0 = 1$, find, to 4 significant figures, the value of α.   [4]

(c) Prove that your answer is accurate to 4 significant figures.   [2]

(d) Hence find, to 3 significant figures, the minimum value of y.   [2]

2 $f(x) = x^3 - 6x + 2$

(a) Show that the equation $f(x) = 0$ has a solution in the interval $2 < x < 3$.   [2]

(b) Use the iteration formula $x_{n+1} = \sqrt{\left(6 - \dfrac{2}{x_n}\right)}$, with $x_0 = 2$, to find the solution to 3 significant figures.   [4]

(c) By sketching two graphs on the same axes, find the total number of solutions.   [2]

3   The iteration formula $x_{n+1} = \sqrt{2x_n + \dfrac{6}{x_n{}^2}}$, with $x_0 = 2$, is used to find a solution, α, of a certain polynomial equation, $P(x) = 0$.

(a) Find $P(x)$.   [2]

(b) Use the formula to find, to 3 significant figures, the value of α.   [4]

4 $f(x) = e^x - 3x - x^2$

The equation $f(x) = 0$ has three solutions.

(a) Show that one of these solutions, α, lies in the interval $0 < \alpha < 1$.   [2]

(b) Find the integer n such that $\dfrac{n}{10} < \alpha < \dfrac{n+1}{10}$.   [3]

The curve C has equation $y = f(x)$. Given that C has a stationary point at the point where $x = \beta$,

(c) show that $1 < \beta < 2$.   [2]

(d) Use an iteration formula of the form $x_{n+1} = \ln(px_n + q)$ to find, to 3 significant figures, the value of β.   [5]

5 $f(x) = 4 - x - \ln 2x$

(a) By sketching two graphs on the same axes, show that the equation $f(x) = 0$ has only one solution.   [4]

The root of the equation $f(x) = 0$ is to be estimated using the iteration formula $x_{n+1} = 4 - \ln 2x_n$, with $x_0 = 2$.

(b) Find the values of $x_1, x_2, x_3, \ldots$ and hence obtain the value, to 3 decimal places, of the root.   [4]

(c) Prove that your answer to part (b) is accurate to 3 decimal places.   [2]

Answers

1.1 Algebra and functions

(1) $\dfrac{1}{x^2 - 4} + \dfrac{3}{x + 2} = \dfrac{4}{5} \rightarrow \dfrac{1}{(x + 2)(x - 2)} + \dfrac{3}{x + 2} = \dfrac{4}{5}$

Factorise the denominator.
Now multiply through by the lowest common denominator, $5(x + 2)(x - 2)$.

$\Rightarrow 5 + 15(x - 2) = 4(x + 2)(x - 2)$ — This clears all the fractions.

$\Rightarrow 15x - 25 = 4(x^2 - 4)$

$\Rightarrow 4x^2 - 15x + 9 = 0$ — Multiplying out and collecting terms.

$\Rightarrow (4x - 3)(x - 3) = 0$ — Factorising.

$\Rightarrow x = \frac{3}{4}$ or $x = 3$.

(2) (a)

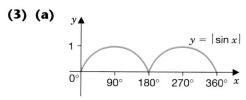

Draw $y = x$ and $y = 2(x - 1)$ and reflect the parts of the graphs below the x-axis in the x-axis.

(b) $|x| = 2|x - 1|$; from the graph there are two cases:

if $x < 1$, $x = 2(1 - x) \rightarrow 3x = 2 \rightarrow x = \frac{2}{3}$

if $x > 1$, $x = 2(x - 1) \rightarrow x = 2$. — $2|x - 1| = 2(x - 1)$ if $x > 1$ and $2(1 - x)$ if $x \leqslant 1$.

(3) (a)

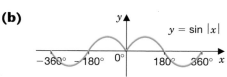

Draw the graph of $y = \sin x$ and reflect the parts of the graph below the x-axis in the x-axis.

(b)

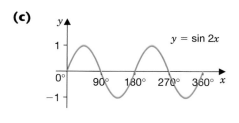

Draw the graph of $y = \sin x$ for $x \geqslant 0$ and reflect this in the y-axis.

(c)

Draw the graph of $y = \sin x$ for $x \geqslant 0$ and reflect this in the y-axis.

To obtain the required graph, stretch the graph of $y = \sin x$ by scale factor $\frac{1}{2}$, parallel to the x-axis.

(4) $\dfrac{2x + 3}{x - 1} + \dfrac{3x - 4}{x + 1} = 3$

Now multiply through by the lowest common denominator, $(x + 1)(x - 1)$.

$\Rightarrow (2x + 3)(x + 1) + (3x - 4)(x - 1) = 3(x - 1)(x + 1)$ — This clears all the fractions.

$\Rightarrow 2x^2 + 5x + 3 + 3x^2 - 7x + 4 = 3x^2 - 3$

$\Rightarrow 2x^2 - 2x + 10 = 0$ — Multiplying out and collecting terms.

'$b^2 - 4ac$' $= 4 - 80 < 0$ so no real roots.

Core 3

(5) $\dfrac{7x-15}{2(x-2)(x-1)} - \dfrac{7}{2x}$

$= \dfrac{x(7x-15) - 7(x-2)(x-1)}{2(x-2)(x-1)x}$ ⟵ Taking the lowest common denominator.

$= \dfrac{7x^2 - 15x - 7(x^2 - 3x + 2)}{2(x-2)(x-1)x}$ ⟵ Multiplying out.

$= \dfrac{7x^2 - 15x - 7x^2 + 21x - 14}{2(x-2)(x-1)x}$ ⟵ Care needed with signs.

$= \dfrac{6x - 14}{2x(x-2)(x-1)}$ ⟵ Simplifying.

$= \dfrac{3x - 7}{x(x-2)(x-1)}$ ⟵ Dividing top and bottom by 2 (lowest terms required).

(6) (a) Let $y = g(x)$

i.e. $y = 2 - \dfrac{1}{(x+1)}$ ⟵ Now make x the subject.

$\Rightarrow \quad \dfrac{1}{(x+1)} = 2 - y$

$\Rightarrow \quad (x+1) = \dfrac{1}{2-y}$

$\Rightarrow \quad x = \dfrac{1}{2-y} - 1$ ⟵ Since $y = g(x) \Rightarrow g^{-1}(y) = x$.

$\Rightarrow \quad g^{-1}(y) = \dfrac{1}{2-y} - 1$

so $g^{-1}: x \to \dfrac{1}{2-x} - 1, \; x \in \mathbb{R}, \; x \neq 2$ ⟵ We usually define functions in terms of x (but it's not essential).

(b) The range of g = domain of g^{-1}
Hence, range of g is $x \in \mathbb{R}, \; x \neq 2$ ⟵ Since $x = 2$ would give zero in the denominator.

(c) $y = 2 - \dfrac{1}{x+1}$

Horizontal asymptote at $y = 2$ ⟵ Draw these on as dotted lines first.
Vertical asymptote at $x = -1$ When $x = 0, y = 1$.

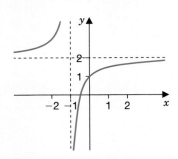

Core 3

14

1.2 Trigonometry

(1) (a) $\text{LHS} = \dfrac{1 + 2\cos\theta + \cos^2\theta + 1 - 2\cos\theta + \cos^2\theta}{\sin^2\theta}$ ⟵ Squaring the brackets and using the common denominator.

$= \dfrac{2 + 2(1 - \sin^2\theta)}{\sin^2\theta}$

$= 4\cosec^2\theta - 2 = \text{RHS}.$

(b) $\text{LHS} = \dfrac{(1 + \cos x)}{\sin x}\dfrac{(1 + \sin x)}{\cos x}$ ⟵ Change everything into sines and cosines.

$= \dfrac{(1 + \cos x)(1 + \sin x)}{\sin x \quad \cos x}$

$= \dfrac{(1 + \cos x)(1 + \sin x)}{\cos x \quad \sin x}$

$= (\sec x + 1)(\cosec x + 1) = \text{RHS}.$

(2) (a) $12\sin\theta + 5\cos\theta = R\sin(\theta + \alpha)$

$= R\sin\theta\cos\alpha + R\cos\theta\sin\alpha$ ⟵ Using the $\sin(A + B)$ formula.

$= (R\cos\alpha)\sin\theta + (R\sin\alpha)\cos\theta$

So $\quad 12 = R\cos\alpha$ ⟵ Since this is an identity we can equate coefficients of $\sin\theta$ and $\cos\theta$.

And $\quad 5 = R\sin\alpha$

$\rightarrow \quad \frac{5}{12} = \tan\alpha$ ⟵ Dividing the equations to eliminate R.

$\rightarrow \quad \alpha = 22.6° \text{ (3 s.f.)}$

And $\quad R^2 = 5^2 + 12^2$ ⟵ Squaring and adding the equations ($\cos^2\alpha + \sin^2\alpha = 1$).

i.e. $\quad R = 13 \text{ (as } R > 0).$

(b) We have $12\sin\theta + 5\cos\theta = 13\sin(\theta + \alpha)$

So $(12\sin\theta + 5\cos\theta)^3 = 13^3\sin^3(\theta + \alpha)$

Hence maximum value is 13^3 when $\theta + \alpha = 90°$ ⟵ Since maximum value of sin is 1.

i.e. 2197 when $\theta = 67.4°$

Hence minimum value is $(-13)^3$ when $\theta + \alpha = 270°$ ⟵ Since minimum value of sin is −1.

i.e. -2197 when $\theta = 247.4°$.

(c) $12\tan\theta + 5 = 4\sec\theta$

$12\sin\theta + 5\cos\theta = 4$ ⟵ Multiplying through by $\cos\theta$.

$13\sin(\theta + \alpha) = 4$ ⟵ Using part (a).

$\sin(\theta + \alpha) = \frac{4}{13}$

$\theta + 22.6° = 377.9° \text{ or } 162.1°$ ⟵ 17.9° would give a θ value which is out of range.

$\theta = 355.3° \text{ or } 139.5°$.

(3) (a) $\sec A + \tan A = 2\cos A$

$\Rightarrow \quad \dfrac{1}{\cos A} + \dfrac{\sin A}{\cos A} = 2\cos A$

$\Rightarrow \quad 1 + \sin A = 2\cos^2 A$ ⟵ Multiplying through by $\cos A$.

$\Rightarrow \quad 1 + \sin A = 2(1 - \sin^2 A)$ ⟵ Using $\sin^2 A + \cos^2 A = 1$.

$\Rightarrow \quad 1 + \sin A = 2 - 2\sin^2 A$

$\Rightarrow \quad 2\sin^2 A + \sin A - 1 = 0$ ⟵ As required.

Core 3

(b) $\sec 2x + \tan 2x = 2\cos 2x$

$\Rightarrow 2\sin^2 2x + \sin 2x - 1 = 0$ ←   Using part **(a)** with $A = 2x$.

$\Rightarrow (2\sin 2x - 1)(\sin 2x + 1) = 0$ ←   Factorising.

$\Rightarrow \sin 2x = \frac{1}{2}$ or $\sin 2x = -1$

$\Rightarrow 2x = \dfrac{\pi}{6}, \dfrac{5\pi}{6}, \dfrac{13\pi}{6}, \dfrac{17\pi}{6}$ or $2x = \dfrac{3\pi}{2}, \dfrac{7\pi}{2}$ ←   Since $0 \leqslant x \leqslant 2\pi$, $0 \leqslant 2x \leqslant 4\pi$.

$\Rightarrow x = \dfrac{\pi}{12}, \dfrac{5\pi}{12}, \dfrac{13\pi}{12}, \dfrac{17\pi}{12}$ or $x = \dfrac{3\pi}{4}, \dfrac{7\pi}{4}$

(4) (a) $2\cos(x + 50°) = \sin(x + 40°)$

$2(\cos x\cos 50° - \sin x\sin 50°) = \sin x\cos 40° + \cos x\sin 40°$

$\Rightarrow 2\cos x\cos 50° - \cos x\sin 40° = \sin x\cos 40° + 2\sin x\sin 50°$ ←   Collecting $\cos x$ terms on L.H.S.

$\Rightarrow \cos x(2\cos 50° - \sin 40°) = \sin x(\cos 40° + 2\sin 50°)$ ←   and $\sin x$ terms on R.H.S.

         Factorising both sides.

$\Rightarrow \dfrac{2\cos 50° - \sin 40°}{\cos 40° + 2\sin 50°} = \dfrac{\sin x}{\cos x} = \tan x$

$\Rightarrow x = 15.6°$ and $195.6°$

(b) $\cos 2x = 2\sin^2 x$

$\Rightarrow 1 - 2\sin^2 x = 2\sin^2 x$ ←   Using the double angle formula.

$\Rightarrow 1 = 4\sin^2 x$ ←   Collecting the terms.

$\Rightarrow \frac{1}{4} = \sin^2 x$

$\Rightarrow \sin x = \frac{1}{2}$ or $-\frac{1}{2}$ ←   Two square roots!

$\Rightarrow x = \dfrac{\pi}{6}, \dfrac{5\pi}{6}$ or $x = \dfrac{7\pi}{6}, \dfrac{11\pi}{6}$

1.3 Exponentials and logarithms

(1) $\quad y = \log_{10}(px + q)$

$\qquad 0 = \log_{10}(3p + q)$ ←   Using the first point.

$\Rightarrow \quad 1 = 3p + q \qquad\qquad (1)$

$\qquad 1 = \log_{10}(4p + q)$ ←   Using the second point.

$\Rightarrow \quad 10 = 4p + q \qquad\qquad (2)$

$\Rightarrow \quad 9 = p$ ←   Subtracting (1) from (2).

$\Rightarrow \quad 1 = 27 + q$

$\Rightarrow \quad -26 = q$

(2) (a) $\quad y = 12 - e^{2x}$ ←   Using the point P.

$\qquad\quad -4 = 12 - e^{2p}$

$\Rightarrow e^{2p} = 16$

$\Rightarrow e^{p} = 4$ (-4 is not possible here as $e^{p} > 0$)   ←   Taking the square root of both sides.

$\Rightarrow p = \ln 4$

$\qquad\quad q = 12 - e^{2\ln 2}$ ←   Using the point Q.

$\qquad\quad q = 12 - e^{\ln 2^2}$

$\qquad\quad q = 12 - e^{\ln 4}$

$\qquad\quad q = 12 - 4$ ← $e^{\ln x} = \ln e^{x} = x$

$\qquad\quad\;\; = 8$

Core 3

(b)

$$y = 12 - e^{2x}$$
$$0 = 12 - e^{2x}$$ ⟵ The x-axis is the line $y = 0$.
$$\Rightarrow \quad e^{2x} = 12$$
$$\Rightarrow \quad \ln e^{2x} = \ln 12$$ ⟵ Taking logs, base e, of both sides.
$$\Rightarrow \quad 2x\ln e = \ln 12$$
$$\Rightarrow \quad 2x = \ln 12$$ ⟵ $\ln e = 1$.
$$\Rightarrow \quad x = \tfrac{1}{2}\ln 12 = \ln\sqrt{12}$$
∴ Crosses at $(\ln\sqrt{12},\ 0)$

(c)

$$y = 12 - e^{2x}$$
$$\frac{dy}{dx} = -2e^{2x}$$ ⟵ We need to find the gradient.

When $\quad x = \ln 4$, ⟵ Using the x-coordinate of P.

$$\frac{dy}{dx} = -2e^{2\ln 4}$$
$$= 2e^{\ln 4^2}$$
$$= -2 \times 16$$ ⟵ $e^{\ln x} = x$.
$$= -32$$

Equation of tangent is

$$y - -4 = -32(x - \ln 4)$$ ⟵ Using $y - y_1 = m(x - x_1)$.
$$y + 4 = -32x + 32\ln 4$$
$$\Rightarrow \quad y = -32x + 32\ln 4 - 4$$

(3) (a)

$$e^{(2x+1)} = 10$$
$$\Rightarrow \quad \ln e^{2x+1} = \ln 10$$ ⟵ Taking logs of both sides, base e.
$$\Rightarrow \quad (2x+1)\ln e = \ln 10$$ ⟵ Using $\ln a^b = b\ln a$.
$$\Rightarrow \quad 2x + 1 = \ln 10$$
$$\Rightarrow \quad x = \tfrac{1}{2}(\ln 10 - 1)$$
$$= 0.65 \ (2\,\text{d.p.})$$

(b) $\ln(9 - 2x) = 2$

$$\Rightarrow 9 - 2x = e^2$$ ⟵ Raise both sides to the power e.
$$\Rightarrow \quad 2x = 9 - e^2$$
$$\Rightarrow \quad x = \tfrac{1}{2}(9 - e^2)$$
$$= 0.81 \ (2\,\text{d.p.})$$

(4)

$$3x - \ln y - 6 = 0$$
$$x + \ln y^2 - 8 = 0$$
$$\Rightarrow \quad 3x - \ln y = 6 \qquad (1)$$ ⟵ Put the unknowns on one side,
$$x + 2\ln y = 8 \qquad (2)$$ the knowns on the other.
$$6x - 2\ln y = 12 \qquad (1) \times 2$$
$$7x = 20$$ ⟵ Adding to eliminate $\ln y$.
$$x = \tfrac{20}{7}$$
$$\Rightarrow \quad \ln y = \tfrac{60}{7} - 6 = \tfrac{18}{7}$$ ⟵ Substituting back into (1).
$$\Rightarrow \quad y = e^{\frac{18}{7}}$$

(5) (a) $\theta = 20 + Ae^{-kt}$

When $t = 0$, $\theta = 70$ ←————————————— *t* is measured from the point
when it starts to cool.

$\Rightarrow \quad 70 = 20 + Ae^{0}$

$\Rightarrow \quad 70 = 20 + A$

$\Rightarrow \quad 50 = A$

(b) $\quad 45 = 20 + 50e^{-4k}$ ←————————————— Using $\theta = 45$ when $t = 4$.

$\Rightarrow \quad 25 = 50e^{-4k}$

$\Rightarrow \quad \frac{1}{2} = e^{-4k}$ ←————————————— Isolating the exponential.

$\Rightarrow \quad 2 = e^{4k}$ ←————————————— Inverting both sides.

$\Rightarrow \quad \ln 2 = \ln e^{4k}$ ←————————————— Now take logs, base e, on both sides.

$\Rightarrow \quad \ln 2 = 4k \ln e$

$\Rightarrow \quad \frac{1}{4}\ln 2 = k$

$\Rightarrow \quad k = 0.173$ (3 d.p.)

1.4 Differentiation

(1) (a)

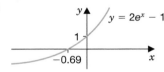

Show where the graph cuts the axes.
When $y = 0$,
$e^x = 0.5 \rightarrow x = \ln 0.5 = -0.69$.

(b) $y = 2e^x - 1$

$\dfrac{dy}{dx} = 2e^x$

When $x = 0$, $\dfrac{dy}{dx} = 2 \rightarrow$ gradient of normal is $-\frac{1}{2}$ ←————— Invert and change the sign to
obtain the gradient of the normal.

When $x = 0$, $y = 1$

Equation of normal is $y - 1 = -\frac{1}{2}(x - 0)$ ←————— Using $y - y_1 = m(x - x_1)$.

i.e. $2y + x - 2 = 0$.

(2) (a)

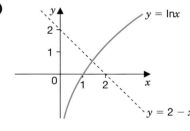

This graph is a reflection of $y = e^x$ in
the line $y = x$ since $\ln x$ is the inverse
of e^x; passing through (1, 0).

(b) $x + \ln x - 2 = 0 \rightarrow \ln x = 2 - x$

The solutions of this equation are the x-coordinates of the points of intersection
of the graphs of $y = \ln x$ and $y = 2 - x$; so draw $y = 2 - x$ on the sketch above.
Clearly only one point of intersection.
Let $f(x) = x + \ln x - 2$; then $f(1.5) = -0.0945\ldots$ and $f(2) = 0.69\ldots$
The change of sign indicates that $1.5 < \alpha < 2$, since the graph of $y = f(x)$ is
continuous.

(3) (a) $x^3 - 8e^{-x} = 0 \rightarrow x^3 = 8e^{-x}$

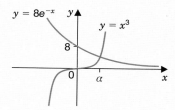

Only one point of intersection at $x = \alpha$.

Draw the graphs of $y = x^3$ and $y = 8e^{-x}$ on the same axes.

(b) Let $f(x) = x^3 - 8e^{-x}$

$f(0) = -8; f(1) = -1.94...; f(2) = 6.91...$

$\rightarrow 1 < \alpha < 2$; hence $n = 1$.

The function changes sign between $x = 1$ and $x = 2$.

(c) $x_2 = 1.0268...$

$x_3 = 1.42...$

$x_4 = 1.2457...$

$x_5 = 1.320...$

$x_6 = 1.287...$

$x_7 = 1.30...$ $\alpha = 1.3$.

It is reasonable to assume that $\alpha = 1.3$ to 1 d.p.,

(d) $f(1.25) = -0.33...$ and $f(1.35) = 0.386...$

$\rightarrow 1.25 < \alpha < 1.35$ i.e. $\alpha = 1.3$ (1 d.p.).

but this is the only way to prove it.

(4) (a) $\dfrac{dN}{dt} = 2000ke^{kt}$

So, $200 = 2000k \rightarrow k = 0.1$.

Rate of increase of the number is the derivative with respect to time.

(b) $N = 2000e^{0.6} = 3644$.

(5) (a) $4x \left(\dfrac{1}{2x^2} \right) = \dfrac{2}{x}$

Using the chain rule.

(b) $2x\cos 4x - 4x^2\sin 4x$

Using the product rule.

(c) $24\sin^2 2x\cos 2x$.

Using the chain rule.

(6) (a) $\dfrac{dy}{dx} = \dfrac{(1 + x^2).2 - 2x.2x}{(1 + x^2)^2} = \dfrac{2(1 - x^2)}{(1 + x^2)^2}$

Using the quotient rule.

(b) When $\dfrac{dy}{dx} = 0, (1 - x^2) = 0$

$\rightarrow x = \pm 1 \rightarrow y = \pm 1$

Points are $(1, 1)$ and $(-1, -1)$

For x just less than 1, $\dfrac{dy}{dx} > 0$

and for x just more than 1, $\dfrac{dy}{dx} < 0$

Hence $(1, 1)$ is a maximum point.

For x just less than -1, $\dfrac{dy}{dx} < 0$

and for x just more than -1, $\dfrac{dy}{dx} > 0$

Hence $(-1, -1)$ is a minimum point.

Stationary points are points where the gradient is 0.

To distinguish between the points consider the sign of $\dfrac{dy}{dx}$ either side of each point.

Core 3

(c) When $x = 0$, $y = 0$

As $x \to +\infty$, $y \to 0^+$; as $x \to -\infty$, $y \to 0^-$

Note that $f(x) = \dfrac{2x}{1 + x^2}$ is an odd function since $f(-x) = -f(x)$. Hence the graph of $y = f(x)$ has rotational symmetry, order 2, about 0.

1.5 Numerical methods

(1) (a) $f(x) = x^3 + x - 6\ln 2x$, $x > 0$

$f'(x) = 3x^2 + 1 - \dfrac{6}{x}$ ← Since $\ln 2x = \ln x + \ln 2$, the derivative of $\ln 2x$ is $\dfrac{1}{x}$.

$f'(1) = 3 + 1 - \dfrac{6}{1} = -2 < 0$

$f'(2) = 12 + 1 - \dfrac{6}{2} = 10 > 0$

Since f' is continuous and changes sign between $x = 1$ and $x = 2$, then $1 < \alpha < 2$ ← A *stationary point* is one where $f'(x) = 0$.

(b) $f'(x) = 0 \Rightarrow 3x^2 + 1 - \dfrac{6}{x} = 0$

$\Rightarrow 3x^3 + x - 6 = 0$ ← Multiplying through by x.

$\Rightarrow 3x^3 = 6 - x$

$\Rightarrow x^3 = 2 - \tfrac{1}{3}x$

$\Rightarrow x = \sqrt[3]{2 - \tfrac{1}{3}x}$

so, $x_{n+1} = \sqrt[3]{2 - \tfrac{1}{3}x_n}$ ← This is the iteration formula. Enter 1 into your calculator; then key in the iteration formula, with x_n replaced by ANS. Press Enter to generate a new value of x.

$x_0 = 1$; $x_1 = 1.1856 \ldots$; $x_2 = 1.17077 \ldots$;

$x_3 = 1.17197 \ldots$; $x_4 = 1.17187 \ldots$;

$x_5 = 1.17188 \ldots$; $x_6 = 1.17188 \ldots$

so, $\alpha = 1.172$ (4 s.f.)

(c) $\alpha = 1.172$ (4 s.f.) $\Rightarrow 1.1715 \le \alpha < 1.1725$

$f'(1.1715) = -0.004 \ldots$ ← This is the only way of *proving* that $\alpha = 1.172$ (4 s.f.).

$f'(1.1725) = +0.006 \ldots$

The sign change $\Rightarrow 1.1715 \le \alpha < 1.1725$

(d) $\therefore y_{\min} = 1.172^3 + 1.172 - 6\ln(2 \times 1.172)$ ← Calculating $f(1.172)$.

$\qquad = -2.33$ (3 s.f.)

(2) (a) $f(x) = x^3 - 6x + 2$ ← We show there is a sign change between $x = 2$ and $x = 3$.

$f(2) = 2^3 - 6 \times 2 + 2$

$\qquad = -2$

$f(3) = 3^3 - 6 \times 3 + 2$

$\qquad = 11$

Since f is continuous, the sign change $\Rightarrow 2 < $ solution < 3

(b) $x_{n+1} = \sqrt{6 - \dfrac{2}{x_n}}; x_0 = 2$ ← Use the ANS button on your calculator (see previous question).

$x_1 = 2.236\ldots; x_2 = 2.259\ldots;$

$x_3 = 2.261\ldots; x_4 = 2.2617\ldots$

solution is 2.26 (3 s.f.)

(c) $x^3 - 6x + 2 = 0$

$\Rightarrow x^3 = 6x - 2$

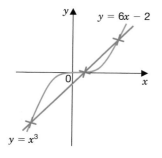

Sketch, on the same axes, $y = x^3$ and $y = 6x - 2$.

There are 3 intersections i.e. there are 3 solutions.

(3) (a) $\qquad x_{n+1} = \sqrt{2x_n + \dfrac{6}{x_n^2}}$ ← Put $x_{n+1} = x_n = x$.

$\Rightarrow \qquad x^2 = 2x + \dfrac{6}{x^2}$ ← Squaring both sides.

$\Rightarrow \qquad x^4 = 2x^3 + 6$ ← Multiplying through x^2.

$\Rightarrow x^4 - 2x^3 - 6 = 0$

Hence, $\quad P(x) = x^4 - 2x^3 - 6$

(b) $x_{n+1} = \sqrt{2x_n + \dfrac{6}{x_n^2}}$

$x_0 = 2; x_1 = 2.345\ldots; x_2 = 2.404\ldots;$

$x_{13} = 2.417\ldots; x_4 = 2.421\ldots;$

$x_5 = 2.421\ldots$

Hence, $\alpha = 2.42$ (3 s.f.)

Use the ANS button on your calculator (see previous question). Note that to *prove* that $\alpha = 2.42$ to 3 s.f. we would need to show that $P(x)$ changes sign between $x = 2.415$ and 2.425.

(4) (a) $f(x) = e^x - 3x - x^2$

$f(0) = 1; f(1) = e - 3 - 1 = -1.28$

Hence, $0 < \alpha < 1$, since f is continuous.

We show that $f(x)$ changes sign between $x = 0$ and $x = 1$.

(b) $n = 0: f(0.1) = 0.795\ldots$

$n = 1: f(0.2) = 0.58\ldots$

$n = 2: f(0.3) = 0.359\ldots$

$n = 3: f(0.4) = 0.131\ldots$

$n = 4: f(0.5) = -0.101\ldots$

Hence, $n = 4$ ← Since there is a sign change.

(c) $f'(x) = e^x - 3 - 2x$ ←

$f'(1) = e - 3 - 2 = -2.28$

$f'(2) = e^2 - 3 - 4 = 0.389$

Hence, $1 < \beta < 2$

A *stationary point* is one where $f'(x) = 0$. We show that $f'(x)$ changes sign between $x = 1$ and $x = 2$. Hence, $f'(x) = 0$ for $1 < \beta < 2$.

Core 3

(d) $x_{n+1} = \ln(px_n + q)$

$f'(x) = 0 \implies e^x - 3 - 2x = 0$ ◄———— **Rearrange to make e^x the subject of this equation.**

$\implies e^x = 2x + 3$

$\implies x = \ln(2x + 3)$

Hence, $p = 2$; $q = 3$

$x_{n+1} = \ln(2x_n + 3)$; ◄———— **Since $f'(2)$ is closer to 0 than $f'(1)$ is, use 2 as the first approximation.**

Take $x_0 = 2$

$x_1 = 1.945 \ldots$; $x_2 = 1.93 \ldots$;

$x_3 = 1.925 \ldots$; $x_4 = 1.924 \ldots$;

$x_{15} = 1.924 \ldots$

Hence, $\beta = 1.92$ (3 s.f.) ◄———— **Again, to *prove* that $\beta = 1.92$ to 3 s.f., we would need to show that there is a sign change for $f'(x)$ between $x = 1.915$ and $x = 1.925$. i.e. $f'(1.915) \times f'(1.925) < 0$ (one is positive, one is negative).**

(5) (a) $f(x) = 4 - x - \ln 2x$

$f(x) = 0$

$\implies 4 - x - \ln 2x = 0$

$\implies \qquad 4 - x = \ln 2x$ ◄———— **We sketch $y = 4 - x$ and $y = \ln 2x$ on the same axes.**

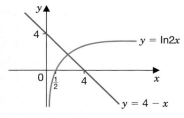

Since there is only one intersection, $f(x) = 0$ has only one solution.

(b) $x_{n+1} \qquad = 4 - \ln 2x_n$; $x_0 = 2$ ◄———— **Use the ANS button on your calculator (as outlined above) to generate these values.**

$x_1 = 2.61 \ldots$; $x_2 = 2.34 \ldots$;

$x_3 = 2.45 \ldots$; $x_4 = 2.40 \ldots$;

$x_5 = 2.42 \ldots$; $x_6 = 2.41 \ldots$;

$x_1 = 2.42 \ldots$; $x_8 = 2.42 \ldots$;

$x_9 = 2.422 \ldots$; $x_{10} = 2.422 \ldots$

root $= 2.422$ (3 d.p.)

(c) $f(2.4215) = 0.00096$; $f(2.4225) = -0.004$

Hence, root is 2.422 (3 d.p.)

Chapter 2

Core 4

Questions with model answers

C grade candidate – mark scored 7/12

Examiner's Commentary

(1) The vector equations of two straight lines are:

$r = 5i + 3j − 2k + t(i − 2j + 2k)$ and $r = pi − 11j + 14k + s(−3i − 4j + 5k)$, where p is a constant.

Given that the two lines meet, find

?

For help see
Revise A2
Study Guide
section 1

(a) the position vector of the point of intersection, [5]

$3 − 2t = −11 − 4s, \quad −2 + 2t = 14 + 5s$ ← Correct.

add the equations: $1 = 3 + s$ ← Correct.

$\Rightarrow s = −2$ ← Correct.

$\Rightarrow t = 3$ ← Correct

$\therefore$ p.v. of point is $8i − 3j − 4k$ ← sign error (should be +4k), **4/5 scored.**

(b) the value of p, [2]

$p − 3s = 8$ ← Method correct.

and $s = −2 \Rightarrow p = 14$ ← Error here, **1/2 scored.**

(c) the angle between the lines. [5]

$(i − 2j + 2k) \cdot (−3i − 4j + 5k)$ ← Candidate is unable to proceed, **2/5 scored.**

$= −3 + 8 + 10 = 15$

GRADE BOOSTER

It is essential that, in order to avoid careless errors, each line of working is checked before proceeding to the next line.

(1) Given that

$$f(x) \equiv \frac{11 - 5x^2}{(x + 1)(2 - x)}$$

(a) find constants A and B such that $f(x) \equiv 5 + \dfrac{A}{(x + 1)} + \dfrac{B}{(2 - x)}$. **[5]**

For help see
Revise A2
Study Guide
section 1

$$\frac{11 - 5x^2}{(x + 1)(2 - x)} = 5 + \frac{A}{(x + 1)} + \frac{B}{(2 - x)}$$

$$11 - 5x^2 = 5(x + 1)(2 - x) + A(2 - x) + B(x + 1)$$

$$x = 2: \quad -9 = 3B \rightarrow B = -3$$

$$x = -1: \quad 6 = 3A \rightarrow A = 2.$$

> Correct – clearing the fractions is the best way to start.
>
> This is an identity so we can put in any value of x – the two values chosen make each bracket in turn zero, **5/5 scored**.

Given that x is so small that x^3 and higher powers of x may be ignored,

(b) find the series expansion of $f(x)$ in ascending powers of x up to and including the term in x^2. **[7]**

$$f(x) = 5 + 2(1 + x)^{-1} - 3(2 - x)^{-1}$$

$$= 5 + 2(1 + x)^{-1} - 3.2\left(1 - \frac{x}{2}\right)^{-1}$$

$$= 5 + 2(1 + (-1)x + (-1)(-2)x^2)$$

$$- 6\left(1 + (-1)\left(-\frac{x}{2}\right) + (-1)(-2)\left(-\frac{x}{2}\right)^2\right)$$

$$= 5 + 2(1 + x + x^2) - 6\left(1 + -\frac{x}{2} + \frac{x^2}{2}\right)$$

$$= 1 - x - x^2.$$

> Correct – writing the partial fractions in this form allows the candidate to use the Binomial Theorem – note that the 2 must be taken out as a factor first but the candidate has forgotten that it should be 2^{-1}.
>
> Writing it out in full to start with is always a good idea, particularly the brackets around the negative and fractional terms, **5/7 scored**.
>
> Incorrect final answer due to the earlier error – the candidate could have checked the constant in the final answer by putting $x = 0$ i.e. $f(0) = \frac{11}{2}$ but putting $x = 0$ in the series expansion gives 1!

Core 4

Exam practice questions

2.1 Algebra and functions

1 $f(x) = \dfrac{x + 4}{(x + 2)(x + 1)^2}$

    (a) Express $f(x)$ in partial fractions.   **[5]**

    (b) Find the value of $f'(1)$.   **[5]**

2 $f(x) = \dfrac{x^2 + 6x + 7}{(x + 3)(x + 2)}.$

  Given that $f(x) \equiv A + \dfrac{B}{x + 3} + \dfrac{C}{x + 2},$

    (a) find the values of the constants A, B and C.   **[5]**

    (b) Show that $\displaystyle\int_0^2 f(x)\,dx = 2 + \ln\left(\dfrac{25}{18}\right).$ **[6]**

3 **(a)** Express $\dfrac{1}{(x + 3)(x + 1)}$ in partial fractions.   **[4]**

    (b) Hence find the general solution of the differential equation

           $\dfrac{dy}{dx} = \dfrac{y}{(x + 3)(x + 1)}, x > -1.$ **[5]**

    (c) Given that when $x = 1$, $y = 2$, express the solution in the form $y^2 = f(x)$.   **[3]**

4 Find the values of the following integrals:

    (a) $\displaystyle\int_3^4 \dfrac{1}{x^2 - 3x + 2}\,dx,$ **[6]**

    (b) $\displaystyle\int_0^1 \dfrac{3}{4 - x^2}\,dx.$ **[6]**

Answers on pages 31–42 Answers on pages 31–42 Answers on pages 31–42

2.2 Coordinate geometry of the (x, y) plane

1 **(a)** Sketch the graph of $y = (x + 2)(x - 1)$. [3]

(b) Hence sketch the graph of $y = \dfrac{1}{(x + 2)(x - 1)}$, giving the equations of any asymptotes. [4]

2 Find the equation of the normals to the curve whose equation is $y^2 + 3xy + 4x^2 = 37$ at the points where $x = 4$. [15]

3 A curve C has parametric equations

$$x = 2t + 3, \quad y = t^3 - 4t.$$

The point P has parameter $t = -1$ and the line l is the tangent to C at P. The line l also cuts the curve at the point Q.

(a) Show that an equation for l is $x + 2y - 7 = 0$. [9]

(b) Find the coordinates of Q. [6]

4 A circle is given parametrically by the equations

$$x = a(2 + \cos t), \quad y = a(3 + \sin t), \quad 0 \leqslant t \leqslant 2\pi$$

where a is a positive constant.

(a) Find a Cartesian equation of the circle. [4]

(b) Find the centre and radius of the circle. [2]

5 A curve C has parametric equations

$$x = t + 1, \quad y = 1 - t^2.$$

(a) Find the area of the region R bounded by C and the x-axis. [4]

(b) Find the volume of the solid formed when R is rotated through one revolution about the x-axis. [5]

2.3 Sequences and series

1 **(a)** $f(x) \equiv \dfrac{1 + 2x}{(6x^2 + 1)(1 - 3x)}$

Express $f(x)$ in partial fractions. [6]

(b) Hence, or otherwise, expand $f(x)$ in ascending powers of x as far as the term in x^3. [5]

(c) State the range of values of x for which the expansion is valid. [3]

Answers on pages 31–42 Answers on pages 31–42 Answers on pages 31–42

2 **(a)** Expand $(4 - 2x)^{\frac{1}{2}}$ in ascending powers of x, up to the term in x^3. [4]

(b) State the range of values of x for which your expansion is valid. [2]

(c) By putting $x = \frac{3}{8}$ in your expansion, find $\sqrt{13}$ to 1 d.p. [4]

3 In the expansion of $(px + 1)^n$ in ascending powers of x, the coefficients of x and x^2 are -6 and 27 respectively.

(a) Find the value of p and the value of n. [5]

(b) Find the coefficient of x^3. [2]

(c) Find the range of values of x for which the expansion is valid. [1]

4 Given that the coefficients of x and x^2 in the expansion of

$$(1 + ax + bx^2)^{-2}$$

in ascending powers of x, are 4 and 14 respectively, find the values of a and b. [7]

2.4 Differentiation

1 Given that $2xy = e^x + e^{2y}$, find $\dfrac{dy}{dx}$. [5]

2 The curve C has parametric equations

$$x = \frac{t}{1 - t}, \, y = \frac{t^2}{1 - t}, \, t \neq 1.$$

(a) Find an expression for $\dfrac{dy}{dx}$ in terms of t. [5]

(b) Find the equation of the normal to C at the point where $t = \frac{1}{2}$. [4]

3 **(a)** Show that the equation of the tangent to the curve with equation $y = 2^x$ at the point where $x = 2$ is

$$y = x\ln 16 + (4 - \ln 256).$$ [4]

(b) Find the area enclosed between this tangent, the curve with equation $y = 2^x$ and the y-axis. [5]

4 The value £V of a car after t years is given by the formula

$$V = 10\,000 \times 0.8^t.$$

(a) Find the value of the car when it was new. [1]

(b) Find the rate, giving your answer to 3 significant figures, at which the car was losing value after 2 years, stating the units of your answer. [4]

(c) Find a first order differential equation satisfied by V. [2]

2.5 Integration

1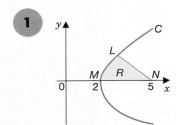

The curve C shown in the diagram has parametric equations

$$x = t + \frac{1}{t}, y = t - \frac{1}{t}, t > 0$$

(a) Find $\dfrac{dy}{dx}$ in terms of t. [4]

(b) Show that the Cartesian equation of C is $x^2 - y^2 = 4$. [3]

The point L on C has coordinates $(2\frac{1}{2}, 1\frac{1}{2})$ and the point M on C has coordinates $(2, 0)$. The point N has coordinates $(5, 0)$. The region R is bounded by the lines MN and LN and the arc LM of the curve C. The region R is rotated through 2π about the x-axis to form a solid of revolution.

(c) Find the volume of the solid, leaving your answer in terms of π. [6]

2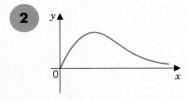

The diagram shows the curve with equation $y = 2xe^{-\frac{x}{2}}$.

(a) Find the coordinates of the turning point on the curve. [6]

(b) The region R is bounded by the curve, the x-axis and the line $x = 2$. Find the area of R. [6]

3 **(a)** Use the substitution $u^2 = x - 1$ to find $\int x\sqrt{x - 1}\, dx$. [8]

(b) Use integration by parts to find $\int x(2x + 1)^{-\frac{1}{2}} dx$. [4]

(c) Find $\int \tan^2 2x\, dx$. [3]

4 (a) Given that $y = x\sqrt{(x + 1)}$, show that

$$\frac{dy}{dx} = \frac{3x + 2}{2\sqrt{(x + 1)}}$$

[4]

(b) Hence, or otherwise, evaluate

$$\int_3^8 \frac{3x + 2}{2\sqrt{(x + 1)}}\,dx$$

[4]

5 Evaluate the following integrals:

(a) $\displaystyle\int_0^1 x^2 e^{-2x}\,dx$

[5]

(b) $\displaystyle\int_0^1 \sin^2 3x\,dx$

[5]

6

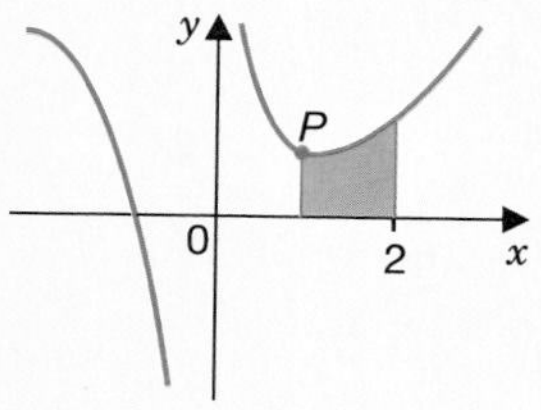

The figure shows part of the curve with equation $y = x^2 + \dfrac{2}{x}$.

(a) Find the coordinates of P.

[2]

(b) Find the volume generated when the shaded region is rotated through 2π around the x-axis.

[5]

7 Evaluate the integral $\displaystyle\int_{\sqrt{3}}^2 \frac{6x}{x^2 - 1}\,dx$.

[5]

8 $A = \displaystyle\int_0^{0.5} \frac{1}{\sqrt{1 - x^2}}\,dx$

Find the value of A using the substitution $x = \sin u$.

[5]

Core 4

Answers on pages 31–42 Answers on pages 31–42 Answers on pages 31–42

2.6 Vectors

1 A line L_1 passes through the point P with position vector $5\mathbf{i} + 3\mathbf{j}$ and the point Q with position vector $-2\mathbf{i} - 4\mathbf{j} + 7\mathbf{k}$.

  (a) Find an equation of the line. [3]

  A second line L_2 has equation $\mathbf{r} = \mathbf{i} - 3\mathbf{j} - 4\mathbf{k} + \lambda\,(\mathbf{i} + 2\mathbf{j} + 3\mathbf{k})$ where λ is a parameter.

  (b) Show that L_1 and L_2 are perpendicular. [2]

  (c) Show that L_1 and L_2 meet and find the position vector of the point of intersection. [5]

  The point R has position vector $2\mathbf{i} - \mathbf{j} - \mathbf{k}$.

  (d) Show that R lies on L_2. [1]

  The point S is the image of R after reflection in the line L_1.

  (e) Find the position vector of S. [3]

2 The line L passes through the point with position vector $(\mathbf{i} + \mathbf{j} - \mathbf{k})$ and is parallel to the vector $(2\mathbf{i} - \mathbf{j})$.

  (a) Find the equation of L. [2]

  The line M passes through the points with position vectors $(\mathbf{i} + \mathbf{j} - \mathbf{k})$ and $(3\mathbf{i} - 2\mathbf{j} + \mathbf{k})$.

  (b) Find, to the nearest degree, the acute angle between L and M. [8]

3 The points P and Q have position vectors $(7\mathbf{i} + \mathbf{j} + 7\mathbf{k})$ and $(4\mathbf{i} - 11\mathbf{j} + 4\mathbf{k})$ respectively, referred to the origin O.

  (a) Find a vector equation for the line PQ. [4]

  (b) Find the position vector of the point N on PQ such that ON is perpendicular to PQ. [5]

  (c) Deduce the perpendicular distance of the line PQ from the origin. [2]

Answers on pages 31–42 Answers on pages 31–42 Answers on pages 31–42

Answers

2.1 Algebra and functions

(1) (a) Let $\dfrac{x+4}{(x+2)(x+1)^2} \equiv \dfrac{A}{x+2} + \dfrac{B}{x+1} + \dfrac{C}{(x+1)^2}$ ← This can be quoted.

$x + 4 \equiv A(x+1)^2 + B(x+2)(x+1) + C(x+2)$ ← Multiplying by $(x+2)(x+1)^2$ on both sides to clear the fractions.

Put $x = -1$: $3 = C$

Put $x = -2$: $2 = A$

Equating constants: $4 = A + 2B + 2C$ ← Check: Coefficients of x^2: –

$\qquad\qquad\qquad\qquad -2 = B$ $\qquad 0 = A + B$.

(b) $f(x) = \dfrac{2}{x+2} - \dfrac{2}{x+1} + \dfrac{3}{(x+1)^2}$

$\qquad = 2(x+2)^{-1} - 2(x+1)^{-1} + 3(x+1)^{-2}$ ← Write each term as a power.

$f'(x) = -2(x+2)^{-2} + 2(x+1)^{-2} - 6(x+1)^{-3}$ ← Differentiating.

$f'(1) = -2 \cdot 3^{-2} + 2 \cdot 2^{-2} - 6 \cdot 2^{-3}$

$\qquad = -\frac{2}{9} + \frac{2}{4} - \frac{6}{8}$

$\qquad = -\frac{17}{36}$

(2) (a) $A + \dfrac{B}{x+3} + \dfrac{C}{x+2} \equiv \dfrac{x^2 + 6x + 7}{(x+3)(x+2)}$

$A(x+3)(x+2) + B(x+2) + C(x+3) \equiv x^2 + 6x + 7$ ← Multiplying both sides by $(x+3)(x+2)$.

Put $x = -3$: $\qquad\qquad\qquad -B = 9 - 18 + 7$

$\qquad\qquad\qquad\qquad\qquad\quad B = 2$

Put $x = -2$: $\qquad\qquad\qquad C = 4 - 12 + 7$

$\qquad\qquad\qquad\qquad\qquad\quad C = -1$

Equate coefficients of x^2: $\qquad A = 1$ ← Check constants:

$\qquad\qquad\qquad\qquad\qquad\qquad\qquad 6A + 2B + 3C = 7$

$\qquad\qquad\qquad\qquad\qquad\qquad\qquad 6 + 4 - 3 = 7$ ✓

(b) $\displaystyle\int_0^2 f(x)\,dx = \int_0^2 \left(1 + \dfrac{2}{x+3} - \dfrac{1}{x+2}\right) dx$ ← From part **(a)**.

$\qquad = [x + 2\ln(x+3) - \ln(x+2)]_0^2$ ← Integrating each term.

$\qquad = (2 + 2\ln5 - \ln4) - (2\ln3 - \ln2)$ ← Substituting in the limits.

$\qquad = 2 + \ln5^2 - \ln4 - \ln3^2 + \ln2$

$\qquad = 2 + \ln\left(\dfrac{5^2 \times 2}{4 \times 3^2}\right)$ ← Combining the logs.

$\qquad = 2 + \ln\left(\dfrac{50}{36}\right)$

$\qquad = 2 + \ln\left(\dfrac{25}{18}\right)$ ← As required.

(3) (a) Let $\dfrac{1}{(x+3)(x+1)} \equiv \dfrac{A}{x+3} + \dfrac{B}{x+1}$ ← This is quotable (and needs to be learned!).

$\Rightarrow \qquad\qquad 1 \equiv A(x+1) + B(x+3)$ ← Multiplying both sides by $(x+3)(x+1)$.

Put $x = -1$: $1 = 2B \Rightarrow B = \frac{1}{2}$

Put $x = -3$: $1 = -2A \Rightarrow A = -\frac{1}{2}$

So, $\dfrac{1}{(x+3)(x+1)} \equiv \dfrac{-1}{2(x+3)} + \dfrac{1}{2(x+1)}$

(b) $\dfrac{dy}{dx} = \dfrac{y}{(x+3)(x+1)}$

$\displaystyle\int \dfrac{dy}{y} = \int \dfrac{dx}{(x+3)(x+1)}$ ←—— Separating the variables and integrating both sides.

$\ln y = \displaystyle\int \left(\dfrac{-1}{2(x+3)} + \dfrac{1}{2(x+1)} \right) dx$ ←—— From part **(a)**.

$\ln y = \frac{1}{2}(-\ln(x+3) + \ln(x+1) + \ln c)$ ←—— c is an arbitrary constant.

$2\ln y = \ln \dfrac{c(x+1)}{(x+3)}$ ←—— Combining the logs.

$\ln y^2 = \ln \dfrac{c(x+1)}{(x+3)}$

$y^2 = \dfrac{c(x+1)}{(x+3)}$ ←—— This is the general solution.

(c) $x = 1,\, y = 2{:}\ 4 = \dfrac{c \times 2}{4} \Rightarrow c = 8$ ←—— Using the given values.

So, $y^2 = \dfrac{8(x+1)}{(x+3)}$ ←—— This is a particular solution.

(4) (a) $\displaystyle\int_3^4 \dfrac{1}{x^2 - 3x + 2}\, dx$

$= \displaystyle\int_3^4 \dfrac{1}{(x-1)(x-2)}\, dx$ ←—— First factorise the denominator.

Let $\dfrac{1}{(x-1)(x-2)} \equiv \dfrac{A}{x-1} + \dfrac{B}{x-2}$ ←—— To be able to integrate we must first split into partial fractions.

$\Rightarrow\qquad 1 \equiv A(x-2) + B(x-1)$

Put $x = 2{:}\ 1 = B$

Put $x = 1{:}\ 1 = -A \Rightarrow A = -1$

$\displaystyle\int_3^4 \left(\dfrac{1}{x-2} - \dfrac{1}{x-1} \right) dx$ ←—— Replacing the integrand by the partial fractions.

$= [\ln(x-2) - \ln(x-1)]_3^4$ ←—— Integrating.

$= \left[\ln\left(\dfrac{x-2}{x-1}\right) \right]_3^4$ ←—— Combine the logs first.

$= \ln\tfrac{2}{3} - \ln\tfrac{1}{2}$

$= \ln(\tfrac{2}{3} \times \tfrac{2}{1}) = \ln\tfrac{4}{3}$

(b) $\displaystyle\int_0^1 \dfrac{3}{4 - x^2}\, dx$

$= \displaystyle\int_0^1 \dfrac{3}{(2+x)(2-x)}\, dx$ ←—— Factorise the denominator first.

$= \displaystyle\int_0^1 \dfrac{3}{4}\left(\dfrac{1}{2+x} + \dfrac{1}{2-x} \right) dx$ ←—— Split into partial fractions (check this yourself).

$= \tfrac{3}{4}[\ln(2+x) - \ln(2-x)]_0^1$ ←—— Leave the constant, $\tfrac{3}{4}$, out. Note the $-$ve sign (the derivative of the bracket).

$= \dfrac{3}{4}\left[\ln\dfrac{(2+x)}{(2-x)} \right]_0^1$ ←—— Combine the logs first.

$= \tfrac{3}{4}(\ln\tfrac{3}{1} - \ln\tfrac{2}{2})$ ←—— Now put the limits in.

$= \tfrac{3}{4}\ln 3$

2.2 Coordinate geometry of the (x, y) plane

(1) (a) When $y = 0$

$(x + 2)(x - 1) = 0 \rightarrow x = -2$ or 1

When $x = 0$, $y = -2$

There is a turning point at $x = \dfrac{-2 + 1}{2} = -\dfrac{1}{2}$

then $y = -\dfrac{9}{4}$

— The curve is a parabola; find where it crosses the axes by putting $y = 0$ and $x = 0$.

— The turning point is on the line of symmetry.

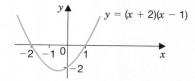

$y = (x + 2)(x - 1)$

(b) There are vertical asymptotes at $x = -2$ and $x = 1$ and a horizontal asymptote at $y = 0$.
The turning point is again on the line of symmetry
i.e. $x = -\frac{1}{2}$ but $y = -\frac{4}{9}$ (the reciprocal of the value in **(a)**).

— Where $y = 0$, since as $x \rightarrow \infty$, $y \rightarrow 0$.

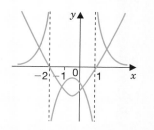

— Note the relationship between the two graphs. They cross when $y = \dfrac{1}{y}$ when $y = \pm 1$.

(2) $y^2 + 3xy + 4x^2 = 37$

When $x = 4$, $y^2 + 12y + 64 = 37$

$y^2 + 12y + 27 = 0$

$(y + 3)(y + 9) = 0$

$y = -3$ or -9 i.e. points are $A(4, -3)$ and $B(4, -9)$.

$y^2 + 3xy + 4x^2 = 37$

$2y\dfrac{dy}{dx} + 3\left(x\dfrac{dy}{dx} + y\right) + 8x = 0$

$\dfrac{dy}{dx}(2y + 3x) = -(8x + 3y)$

$\dfrac{dy}{dx} = -\dfrac{(8x + 3y)}{(2y + 3x)}$

At A, $\dfrac{dy}{dx} = -\dfrac{23}{6}$; at B, $\dfrac{dy}{dx} = \dfrac{5}{6}$

At A, gradient of normal is $\frac{6}{23}$

So $y - -3 = \frac{6}{23}(x - 4)$

$23y - 6x + 93 = 0$

At B, gradient of normal is $-\frac{6}{5}$

So $y - -9 = -\frac{6}{5}(x - 4)$

$5y + 6x + 21 = 0$

— First find all the points where $x = 4$.

— Differentiating with respect to x.

— Collecting terms in $\dfrac{dy}{dx}$ on one side and the rest on the other.

— Using the coordinates of A and B.

— Invert the gradient of the tangent and change the sign.

— Using $y - y_1 = m(x - x_1)$.

— Check that the coordinates of A satisfy this equation.

— Check that the coordinates of B satisfy this equation

(3) (a) When $t = -1$, $x = 1$ and $y = 3$ ← First find the coordinates of P.

$\dfrac{dy}{dt} = 3t^2 - 4$; $\dfrac{dx}{dt} = 2$ ← We need to find the gradient of the curve at P.

When $t = -1$, $\dfrac{dy}{dt} = -1$

So $\dfrac{dy}{dx} = -\dfrac{1}{2}$ ← $\dfrac{dy}{dx} = \dfrac{dy}{dt} \bigg/ \dfrac{dx}{dt}$.

Equation of tangent is $y - 3 = -\frac{1}{2}(x - 1)$ ← Using $y - y_1 = m(x - x_1)$.

$2y - 6 = -x + 1$ i.e. $x + 2y - 7 = 0$.

(b) $(2t + 3) + 2(t^3 - 4t) - 7 = 0$ ← Substituting for x and y in the tangent equation; two of the roots of this equation are –1 (twice) since the tangent touches the curve at $t = -1$.

$2t^3 - 6t - 4 = 0$ i.e. $t^3 - 3t - 2 = 0$

$(t + 1)^2(t - 2) = 0$ ← The third factor can be found by inspection.

So $t = 2$ is the parameter of Q

So $x = 7$, $y = 0$

i.e. Q has coordinates (7, 0).

(4) (a) $x = a(2 + \cos t)$; $y = a(3 + \sin t)$ ← We need to eliminate the parameter t.

$\dfrac{x}{a} - 2 = \cos t$; $\dfrac{y}{a} - 3 = \sin t$ ← Isolate the cos and sin terms.

So, $\left(\dfrac{x}{a} - 2\right)^2 + \left(\dfrac{y}{a} - 3\right)^2 = 1$ ← Using $\cos^2 t + \sin^2 t = 1$.

i.e. $\left(\dfrac{x - 2a}{a}\right)^2 + \left(\dfrac{y - 3a}{a}\right)^2 = 1$

$(x - 2a)^2 + (y - 3a) = a^2$ ← Multiplying through by a^2.

(b) Centre is $(2a, 3a)$; radius a ← Comparing with $(x - x_1)^2 + (y - y_1)^2 = r^2$.

(5) (a) $x = t + 1$; $y = 1 - t^2$ ← First find where the curve cuts the x-axis.

Put $y = 0$: $0 = 1 - t^2 \Rightarrow t = \pm 1$

Area $= \displaystyle\int_{x_1}^{x_2} y\, dx = \int_{t=-1}^{t=+1} y\, \dfrac{dx}{dt} \cdot dt$ ← Change the integral in x to an integral in t.

$= \displaystyle\int_{-1}^{1} (1 - t^2) \times 1 \times dt$

$= \left[t - \dfrac{t^3}{3}\right]_{-1}^{1} = (1 - \tfrac{1}{3}) - (-1 + \tfrac{1}{3})$ ← Integrating with respect to t and putting in the limits.

$= \tfrac{2}{3} + \tfrac{2}{3}$

$= \tfrac{4}{3}$

(b) Volume $= \pi \int_{x_1}^{x_2} y^2 \mathrm{d}x$

$= \pi \int_{-1}^{1} y^2 \frac{\mathrm{d}x}{\mathrm{d}t} \cdot \mathrm{d}t$ ←——————— Change the integral in x to an integral in t.

$= \pi \int_{-1}^{1} (1 - t^2)^2 \times 1 \times \mathrm{d}t$

$= \pi \int_{-1}^{1} (1 - 2t^2 + t^4)\mathrm{d}t$ ←——————— First multiply out the brackets.

$= \pi \left[t - \frac{2}{3}t^3 + \frac{t^5}{5} \right]_{-1}^{1}$ ←——————— Integrating with respect to t.

$= \pi \{(1 - \frac{2}{3} + \frac{1}{5}) - (-1 + \frac{2}{3} - \frac{1}{5})\}$

$= \pi(\frac{8}{15} - -\frac{8}{15})$

$= \dfrac{16\pi}{15}$

2.3 Sequences and series

(1) (a) Let $\dfrac{1 + 2x}{(6x^2 + 1)(1 - 3x)} \equiv \dfrac{Ax + B}{(6x^2 + 1)} + \dfrac{C}{(1 - 3x)}$

$1 + 2x = (Ax + B)(1 - 3x) + C(6x^2 + 1)$ ←——————— Multiplying through by $(6x^2 + 1)(1 - 3x)$.

$x = \frac{1}{3} : \frac{5}{3} = C. \frac{5}{3} \rightarrow C = 1$

$-3A + 6C = 0 \rightarrow A = 2$ ←——————— Equating coefficients of x^2.

$1 = B + C \rightarrow B = 0$ ←——————— Equating constant terms.

So $f(x) = \dfrac{2x}{(6x^2 + 1)} + \dfrac{1}{(1 - 3x)}$

(b) $f(x) = 2x(1 + 6x^2)^{-1} + (1 - 3x)^{-1}$ ←——————— Both brackets are already in form $(1 + ...)^n$ so we can use the Binomial Theorem.

$= 2x(1 - 6x^2 + ...) +$

$\left(1 + (-1)(-3x) + \dfrac{(-1)(-2)(-3x)^2}{2!} + \dfrac{(-1)(-2)(-3)(-3x)^3}{3!} + ... \right)$ ←— Write out the series in full first, then simplify.

$= 2x - 12x^3 + 1 + 3x + 9x^2 + 27x^3 + ...$

$= 1 + 5x + 9x^2 + 15x^3 + ...$

(c) First series valid for $|6x^2| < 1$ i.e. $|x| < \dfrac{1}{\sqrt{6}}$ ←——————— Binomial series for $(1 + x)^n$, n not a positive whole number, only valid for $|x| < 1$.

Second series valid for $|-3x| < 1$ i.e. $|x| < \frac{1}{3}$

So both valid for $|x| < \frac{1}{3}$ as $\frac{1}{3} < \dfrac{1}{\sqrt{6}}$ as $3 > \sqrt{6}$.

(2) (a) $(4 - 2x)^{\frac{1}{2}} = \{4(1 - \frac{1}{2}x)\}^{\frac{1}{2}}$ ←——————— Take out the 4 as a factor.

$= 4^{\frac{1}{2}}(1 - \frac{1}{2}x)^{\frac{1}{2}}$

$= 2\left(1 + (\frac{1}{2})(-\frac{1}{2}x) + \dfrac{(\frac{1}{2})(-\frac{1}{2})(-\frac{1}{2}x)^2}{2!} + \dfrac{(\frac{1}{2})(-\frac{1}{2})(-\frac{3}{2})(-\frac{1}{2}x)^3}{3!} + ... \right)$ ←— Write out the series in full first, then simplify.

$= 2(1 - \frac{1}{4}x - \frac{1}{32}x^2 - \frac{1}{128}x^3 + ...)$

$= 2 - \frac{1}{2}x - \frac{1}{16}x^2 - \frac{1}{64}x^3 + ...$

(b) $|-\frac{1}{2}x| < 1 \rightarrow |x| < 2$

(c) $(4 - \frac{3}{4})^{1/2} = 2 - \frac{3}{16} - \frac{9}{1024} - \frac{27}{32768}$ $\longleftarrow$ $(4 - \frac{3}{4})^{1/2} = \sqrt{\left(\frac{13}{4}\right)} = \frac{\sqrt{13}}{}$

i.e. $\sqrt{13} = 2(2 - \frac{3}{16} - \frac{9}{1024} - \frac{27}{32768}) = 3.605... = 3.6$ (1 d.p.).

(3) (a) $(px + 1)^n = (1 + px)^n$ $\longleftarrow$ Reverse the order of the terms as we want to expand in ascending powers of x.

$= 1^n + n \cdot 1^{n-1}(px) + \dfrac{n(n-1)}{2!} \cdot 1^{n-2}(px)^2$

Equating the coefficients of x and x^2.

So, $np = -6$ (1)

$\dfrac{n(n-1)}{2}p^2 = 27$ (2)

$n^2p^2 = 36$ $\longleftarrow$ Squaring equation (1).

$\dfrac{n(n-1)}{2n^2} = \dfrac{27}{36} = \dfrac{3}{4}$ $\longleftarrow$ Now divide to eliminate p.

$2n - 2 = 3n$ $\longleftarrow$ Cancel n and 2.

$-2 = n \Rightarrow p = 3$ from (1)

(b) Coefficient of $x^3 = \dfrac{n(n-1)(n-2)}{3!} p^3$ $\longleftarrow$ A common error is to omit the p^3 term.

$= \dfrac{-2 \times -3 \times -4}{3!} \times 3^3$

$= -108$

(c) Expansion valid for $|px| < 1$ $\longleftarrow$ Since n is *not* a positive integer. (If it was the expansion would be valid for all x.)

$\Rightarrow |3x| < 1 \Rightarrow |x| < \frac{1}{3}$

(4) $(1 + (ax + bx^2))^{-2}$ $\longleftarrow$ Treat $(ax + bx^2)$ as a single term when expanding.

$= 1 + (-2)(ax + bx^2) + \dfrac{(-2)(-3)}{2!}(ax + bx^2)^2 + ...$

$= 1 - 2ax - 2bx^2 + 3(a^2x^2 + ...)$ $\longleftarrow$ Write out in full first.

$= 1 - 2ax + (3a^2 - 2b)x^2 + ...$ $\longleftarrow$ Collecting up the terms.

$-2a = 4; \ 3a^2 - 2b = 14$ $\longleftarrow$ Comparing coefficients.

$\Rightarrow a = -2; \ 12 - 2b = 14$

$\Rightarrow b = -1$

2.4 Differentiation

(1) $2\left(x\dfrac{dy}{dx} + y\right) = e^x + 2\dfrac{dy}{dx}e^{2y}$ $\longleftarrow$ Using the product rule on LHS and chain rule on RHS.

$\dfrac{dy}{dx}(2x - 2e^{2y}) = (e^x - 2y)$ $\longleftarrow$ Collecting the $\dfrac{dy}{dx}$ terms on LHS.

$\dfrac{dy}{dx} = \dfrac{(e^x - 2y)}{(2x - 2e^{2y})}$

(2) (a) $\dfrac{dx}{dt} = \dfrac{(1-t)\,.\,1 - t(-1)}{(1-t)^2} = \dfrac{1}{(1-t)^2}$ ⟵ Using the quotient rule.

$\dfrac{dy}{dt} = \dfrac{(1-t)\,.\,2t - t^2(-1)}{(1-t)^2} = \dfrac{1-t^2}{(1-t)^2}$ ⟵ Using the quotient rule again.

So, $\dfrac{dy}{dx} = \dfrac{dy}{dt} \div \dfrac{dx}{dt} = \dfrac{1-t^2}{(1-t)^2} \times \dfrac{(1-t)^2}{1}$

$= 1 - t^2$

(b) When $t = \frac{1}{2}$, $\dfrac{dy}{dx} = 1 - \frac{1}{4} = \frac{3}{4}$ ⟵ First find the gradient of the tangent.

$\therefore$ Gradient of normal $= -\dfrac{4}{3}$ ⟵ To obtain the gradient of the normal flip the fraction and change its sign.

When $t = \frac{1}{2}$, $x = \dfrac{\frac{1}{2}}{1 - \frac{1}{2}} = 1$; $y = \dfrac{\frac{1}{4}}{1 - \frac{1}{2}} = \frac{1}{2}$ ⟵ We need to find the x and y coordinates at $t = \frac{1}{2}$.

Equation of normal is $y - \frac{1}{2} = -\frac{4}{3}(x - 1)$

$\Rightarrow 6y - 3 = -8x + 8$ ⟵ Using $y - y_1 = m(x - x_1)$.

$\Rightarrow 6y + 8x - 11 = 0$ ⟵ Collecting the terms.

(3) (a) $y = 2^x$

$\dfrac{dy}{dx} = \ln 2\,.\,2^x$ ⟵ Learn this result.

When $x = 2$, $\dfrac{dy}{dx} = 4\ln 2$, $y = 4$

Equation of tangent is

$y - 4 = 4\ln 2(x - 2)$ ⟵ Using $y - y_1 = m(x - x_1)$.

$y = 4\ln 2\,.\,x + (4 - 8\ln 2)$

$= \ln 2^4\,.\,x + (4 - \ln 2^8)$

$= x\ln 16 + (4 - \ln 256)$ ⟵ As required.

(b)

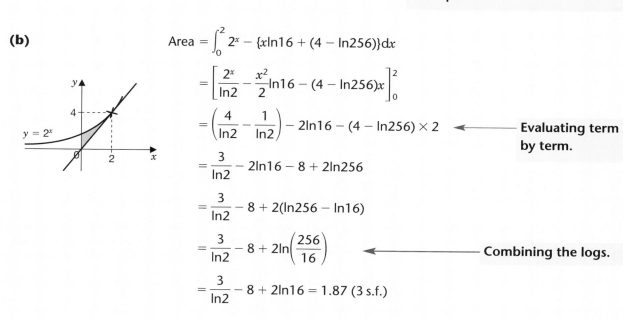

Area $= \displaystyle\int_0^2 2^x - \{x\ln 16 + (4 - \ln 256)\}\,dx$

$= \left[\dfrac{2^x}{\ln 2} - \dfrac{x^2}{2}\ln 16 - (4 - \ln 256)x \right]_0^2$

$= \left(\dfrac{4}{\ln 2} - \dfrac{1}{\ln 2} \right) - 2\ln 16 - (4 - \ln 256) \times 2$ ⟵ Evaluating term by term.

$= \dfrac{3}{\ln 2} - 2\ln 16 - 8 + 2\ln 256$

$= \dfrac{3}{\ln 2} - 8 + 2(\ln 256 - \ln 16)$

$= \dfrac{3}{\ln 2} - 8 + 2\ln\left(\dfrac{256}{16} \right)$ ⟵ Combining the logs.

$= \dfrac{3}{\ln 2} - 8 + 2\ln 16 = 1.87 \text{ (3 s.f.)}$

Core 4

(4) (a) $t = 0$, $V = 10\,000$ i.e. value is £10 000 ←———————— $t = 0$ when car was new.

(b)
$$V = 10\,000 \times 0.8^t$$

$$\frac{dV}{dt} = 10\,000 \times \ln 0.8 \times 0.8^t \qquad (1) \quad \longleftarrow \quad \text{Rate is } \frac{dV}{dt}.$$

When $t = 2$, $\dfrac{dV}{dt} = 10\,000 \times \ln 0.8 \times 0.8^2$

$$= 6400 \times \ln 0.8$$

$$= -1428.1\ldots$$

∴ Rate at which value is going down is £1430 per year after 2 years.

(c) From (1), $\dfrac{dV}{dt} = \ln 0.8\, V$ ←——————— This is a 1st order differential equation.

2.5 Integration

(1) (a) $\dfrac{dx}{dt} = 1 - \dfrac{1}{t^2}$; $\dfrac{dy}{dt} = 1 + \dfrac{1}{t^2}$

$$\frac{dy}{dx} = \left(1 + \frac{1}{t^2}\right)\bigg/\left(1 - \frac{1}{t^2}\right) = (t^2 + 1)/(t^2 - 1) \quad \longleftarrow \quad \frac{dy}{dx} = \frac{dy}{dt}\bigg/\frac{dx}{dt}$$

(b) $x^2 = \left(t + \dfrac{1}{t}\right)^2 = t^2 + 2 + \dfrac{1}{t^2}$ ←——————— To find the Cartesian equation we must eliminate the parameter t.

$$y^2 = \left(t - \frac{1}{t}\right)^2 = t^2 - 2 + \frac{1}{t^2}$$

Subtracting gives $x^2 - y^2 = 4$.

(c) $V = \pi \displaystyle\int_2^{5/2} y^2\, dx$ + volume of cone

$$= \pi \int_2^{5/2} (x^2 - 4)\, dx + \frac{1}{3}\pi\left(\frac{3}{2}\right)^2\left(\frac{5}{2}\right) \quad \longleftarrow \quad \text{Volume of a cone is } \tfrac{1}{3}\pi r^2 h.$$

$$= \pi\left[\frac{1}{3}x^3 - 4x\right]_2^{\frac{5}{2}} + \frac{15\pi}{8}$$

$$= \frac{29\pi}{12}$$

(2) (a) $y = 2xe^{-x/2}$

$$\frac{dy}{dx} = 2e^{-x/2} - xe^{-x/2} \quad \longleftarrow \quad \text{Using the product rule.}$$

$$= (2 - x)\, e^{-x/2} \quad \longleftarrow \quad \text{Factorising.}$$

At a turning point, $0 = (2 - x)e^{-x/2}$

$\rightarrow x = 2$, since $e^{-x/2} > 0$ for all x

When $x = 2$, $y = 4e^{-1}$ i.e. $(2, 4e^{-1})$ is the turning point.

(b) Area $= \displaystyle\int_0^2 y\, dx = \int_0^2 2xe^{-x/2}\, dx$

$$= [2x.(-2e^{-x/2})]_0^2 - \int_0^2 2(-2e^{-x/2})\, dx \quad \longleftarrow \quad \text{Using integration by parts.}$$

$$= -8e^{-1} - [8e^{-x/2}]_0^2$$

$$= 8 - 16e^{-1}$$

(3) (a) $u^2 = x - 1 \rightarrow 2u\dfrac{du}{dx} = 1 \rightarrow 2u\,du = dx$ ⟵ First differentiate the substitution.

$$\int x\sqrt{(x-1)}\,dx = \int (u^2 + 1)\,u\,.2u\,du = 2\int (u^4 + u^2)\,du$$ ⟵ Every part of the integral must be put in terms of u.

$$= 2(\tfrac{1}{5}u^5 + \tfrac{1}{3}u^3) + c$$

$$= \tfrac{2}{15}u^3\,(3u^2 + 5) + c$$ ⟵ Factorise before changing back to x.

$$= \tfrac{2}{15}(x-1)^{3/2}\,(3x - 3 + 5) + c$$

$$= \tfrac{2}{15}(x-1)^{3/2}\,(3x + 2) + c$$ ⟵ The final answer must be in terms of x.

(b) $I = x\,(2x+1)^{1/2} - \int (2x+1)^{1/2}\,dx$ ⟵ Using integration by parts – differentiating the x.

$$= x\,(2x+1)^{1/2} - \tfrac{1}{3}(2x+1)^{3/2} + c$$

(c) $\int \tan^2 2x\,dx = \int (\sec^2 2x - 1)\,dx = \tfrac{1}{2}\tan 2x - x + c$ ⟵ Using $1 + \tan^2 x = \sec^2 x$.

(4) (a) $y = x\sqrt{x+1} = x(x+1)^{\frac{1}{2}}$

$$\dfrac{dy}{dx} = x\,.\tfrac{1}{2}(x+1)^{-\frac{1}{2}} + \sqrt{x+1}\,.1$$ ⟵ Using the Product Rule.

$$= \dfrac{x}{2\sqrt{x+1}} + \sqrt{x+1}$$

$$= \dfrac{x + 2(x+1)}{2\sqrt{x+1}}$$ ⟵ Taking the common denominator.

$$= \dfrac{3x+2}{2\sqrt{x+1}}$$

(b) $\displaystyle\int_3^8 \dfrac{3x+2}{2\sqrt{x+1}}\,dx = [x\sqrt{x+1}]_3^8$ ⟵ Using the result from part **(a)**.

$$= (8 \times 3) - (3 \times 2) = 18$$ ⟵ Putting in the limits.

(5) (a) $\displaystyle\int_0^1 x^2 e^{-2x}\,dx$

$$= [-\tfrac{1}{2}e^{-2x} \cdot x^2]_0^1 - \int_0^1 -\tfrac{1}{2}e^{-2x} \cdot 2x\,dx$$ ⟵ Integrating by parts.

$$= -\tfrac{1}{2}e^{-2} + \int_0^1 xe^{-2x}\,dx$$ ⟵ Simplify as you go along.

$$= -\tfrac{1}{2}e^{-2} + [-\tfrac{1}{2}e^{-2x} \cdot x]_0^1 - \int_0^1 -\tfrac{1}{2}e^{-2x}\,dx$$ ⟵ Integrating by parts again.

$$= -\tfrac{1}{2}e^{-2} - \tfrac{1}{2}e^{-2} + \tfrac{1}{2}\int_0^1 e^{-2x}\,dx$$

$$= -e^{-2} - \tfrac{1}{4}[e^{-2x}]_0^1$$

$$= -e^{-2} - \tfrac{1}{4}(e^{-2} - 1)$$

$$= \tfrac{1}{4} - \tfrac{5}{4}e^{-2}$$

(b) $\dfrac{1}{2}\displaystyle\int_0^{\pi/2} (1 - \cos 6x)\,dx = \tfrac{1}{2}[x - \tfrac{1}{6}\sin 6x]_0^{\pi/2}$

$$= \dfrac{\pi}{4}$$

(6) (a) $y = x^2 + \dfrac{2}{x}$

$y = x^2 + 2x^{-1}$ ⟵ Write each term as a power of x.

$\dfrac{dy}{dx} = 2x - 2x^{-2}$ ⟵ Differentiating.

$2x - 2x^{-2} = 0$ ⟵ The gradient at P is zero.

$\Rightarrow x^3 - 1 = 0$ ⟵ Multiplying through by x^2.

$\Rightarrow x = 1 \Rightarrow y = 1 + \dfrac{2}{1} = 3$

i.e. P is (1, 3)

(b) $V = \pi \displaystyle\int_1^2 y^2 dx$ ⟵ This formula is quotable.

$= \pi \displaystyle\int_1^2 \left(x^2 + \dfrac{2}{x}\right)^2 dx$

$= \pi \displaystyle\int_1^2 (x^4 + 4x + 4x^{-2}) dx$ ⟵ Squaring the bracket.

$= \pi \left[\dfrac{x^5}{5} + 2x^2 - 4x^{-1}\right]_1^2$ ⟵ Integrating term by term.

$= \pi \left\{\dfrac{1}{5}(2^5 - 1^5) + 2(2^2 - 1^2) - 4\left(\dfrac{1}{2} - \dfrac{1}{1}\right)\right\}$ ⟵ Evaluating term by term.

$= \pi \left(\dfrac{31}{5} + 6 + 2\right)$

$= \dfrac{\pi}{5}\left(31 + 40\right) = \dfrac{71\pi}{5}$

(7) $\displaystyle\int_{\sqrt{3}}^2 \dfrac{6x}{x^2 - 1} dx = 3[\ln(x^2 - 1)]_{\sqrt{3}}^2$ ⟵ Using $\displaystyle\int \dfrac{f'(x)}{f(x)} dx = \ln f(x) + c.$

$= 3(\ln 3 - \ln 2)$

$= 3\ln\tfrac{3}{2}$

(8) $A = \displaystyle\int_0^{0.5} \dfrac{1}{\sqrt{1 - x^2}} dx$

$x = \sin u \Rightarrow dx = \cos u \, du$

$\sqrt{1 - x^2} = \sqrt{1 - \sin^2 u} = \cos u$

$x = 0,\ \sin u = 0 \Rightarrow u = 0$

$x = 0.5,\ \sin u = 0.5 \Rightarrow u = \dfrac{\pi}{6}$ ⟵ Note that we must work in radians.

$A = \displaystyle\int_0^{\pi/6} \dfrac{\cos u}{\cos u} du$ ⟵ Substituting into the integral.

$= \displaystyle\int_0^{\pi/6} du$

$= [u]_0^{\pi/6} = \dfrac{\pi}{6}$

2.6 Vectors

(1) **(a)** Direction vector $= (5\mathbf{i} + 3\mathbf{j}) - (-2\mathbf{i} - 4\mathbf{j} + 7\mathbf{k}) = 7\mathbf{i} + 7\mathbf{j} - 7\mathbf{k}$

$\mathbf{r}_1 = (5\mathbf{i} + 3\mathbf{j}) + \mu(\mathbf{i} + \mathbf{j} - \mathbf{k})$ ⟵   We can omit the 7s from the direction vector.

(b) $(\mathbf{i} + \mathbf{j} - \mathbf{k}).(\mathbf{i} + 2\mathbf{j} + 3\mathbf{k}) = 1 + 2 - 3 = 0$ ⟵   Taking the scalar product of the direction vectors of the two lines.
Hence perpendicular.

(c) At intersection,

$(5\mathbf{i} + 3\mathbf{j}) + \mu(\mathbf{i} + \mathbf{j} - \mathbf{k}) = (\mathbf{i} - 3\mathbf{j} - 4\mathbf{k}) + \lambda(\mathbf{i} + 2\mathbf{j} + 3\mathbf{k})$ ⟵ Equating the position vectors.

$5 + \mu = 1 + \lambda$

$\left.\begin{array}{l} 3 + \mu = -3 + 2\lambda \\ 0 - \mu = -4 + 3\lambda \end{array}\right\}$ ⟵   Equating coefficients of i, j and k.

$3 = -7 + 5\lambda$ ⟵   Adding the 2nd and 3rd equations.

$\rightarrow \lambda = 2 \rightarrow \mu = -2$

Check that these values satisfy *all three* equations
p.v. of intersection point is $3\mathbf{i} + \mathbf{j} + 2\mathbf{k}$.

(d) When $\lambda = 1$ in the equation of L_2, $\mathbf{r} = 2\mathbf{i} - \mathbf{j} - \mathbf{k}$,
hence R lies on L_2.

(e)

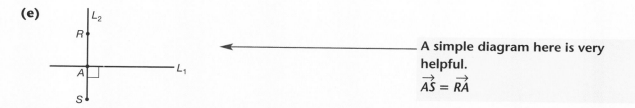

A simple diagram here is very helpful.
$\overrightarrow{AS} = \overrightarrow{RA}$

If A is the point of intersection of L_1 and L_2
then $RA = \mathbf{i} + 2\mathbf{j} + 3\mathbf{k}$, then p.v. of S is given by
$(3\mathbf{i} + \mathbf{j} + 2\mathbf{k}) + (\mathbf{i} + 2\mathbf{j} + 3\mathbf{k}) = 4\mathbf{i} + 3\mathbf{j} + 5\mathbf{k}$.

(2) **(a)** $\mathbf{r} = (\mathbf{i} + \mathbf{j} - \mathbf{k}) + t(2\mathbf{i} - \mathbf{j})$

(b) direction vector of M

$= (3\mathbf{i} - 2\mathbf{j} + \mathbf{k}) - (\mathbf{i} + \mathbf{j} - \mathbf{k})$ ⟵   This gives a vector along the line M.

$= 2\mathbf{i} - 3\mathbf{j} + 2\mathbf{k}$

$(2\mathbf{i} - \mathbf{j}) \cdot (2\mathbf{i} - 3\mathbf{j} + 2\mathbf{k})$ ⟵   The angle between lines L and M is equal to the angle between the 2 direction vectors. We calculate the dot product in 2 different ways and equate.

$= 4 + 3 = 7$

Also, $(2\mathbf{i} - \mathbf{j}) \cdot (2\mathbf{i} - 3\mathbf{j} + 2\mathbf{k})$

$= \sqrt{2^2 + (+1)^2} \cdot \sqrt{2^2 + (-3)^2 + 2^2} \cos\theta$

i.e. $7 = \sqrt{5} \cdot \sqrt{17} \cos\theta$

$\cos\theta = \dfrac{7}{\sqrt{85}} \Rightarrow \theta = 41°$ (nearest degree)

(3) (a) direction vector of the line PQ

$$= \overrightarrow{PQ} = \mathbf{q} - \mathbf{p} = (4\mathbf{i} - 11\mathbf{j} + 4\mathbf{k}) - (7\mathbf{i} + \mathbf{j} + 7\mathbf{k})$$

$$= -3\mathbf{i} - 12\mathbf{j} - 3\mathbf{k}$$

i.e. $\mathbf{i} + 4\mathbf{j} + \mathbf{k}$ ◄─────────────────────── We can divide by -3 as this does not change the direction of the vector.

Equation of PQ is

$$\mathbf{r} = (7\mathbf{i} + \mathbf{j} + 7\mathbf{k}) + t(\mathbf{i} + 4\mathbf{j} + \mathbf{k})$$

$$= (7 + t)\mathbf{i} + (1 + 4t)\mathbf{j} + (7 + t)\mathbf{k}$$ ◄──────────── Collecting $\mathbf{i}$, $\mathbf{j}$ and $\mathbf{k}$ terms.

(b) $\overrightarrow{ON}$ perpendicular $\overrightarrow{PQ}$

$$\Rightarrow \overrightarrow{ON} \cdot \overrightarrow{PQ} = 0$$

$$\Rightarrow \{(7 + t)\mathbf{i} + (1 + 4t)\mathbf{j} + (7 + t)\mathbf{k}\} \cdot (\mathbf{i} + 4\mathbf{j} + \mathbf{k}) = 0$$

$$\Rightarrow 7 + t + 4(1 + 4t) + (7 + t) = 0$$

$$\Rightarrow \quad 7 + t + 4 + 16t + 7 + t = 0$$

$$\Rightarrow \qquad\qquad\qquad\qquad 18t = -18$$

$$\Rightarrow \qquad\qquad\qquad\qquad\quad t = -1$$

Hence, p.v. of N is $6\mathbf{i} - 3\mathbf{j} + 6\mathbf{k}$. ◄─────────── Putting $t = -1$.

(c) Perpendicular distance of the line PQ

from $O = |\overrightarrow{ON}|$

$$= \sqrt{6^2 + (-3)^2 + 6^2}$$

$$= \sqrt{81}$$

$$= 9 \text{ units}$$

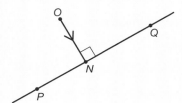

Core 4

42

Questions with model answers

C grade candidate – mark scored 6/10

Examiner's Commentary

(1)

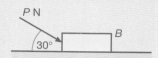

A heavy block *B* of mass 50 kg is pushed along a horizontal surface by a force of magnitude *P* newtons. The force acts at 30° to the surface, as shown in the diagram, and *B* moves in a straight line with constant speed. The block is modelled as a particle and the surface is rough. The coefficient of friction between *B* and the surface is $\frac{1}{2}$.
Find the value of *P*.

[10]

For help see
Revise AS
Study Guide
section 3

$\frac{1}{2}R$ used for friction

1/1 scored.

$R(\rightarrow)$, $P\sin 30° = \frac{1}{2}R$ (1)

Error here – should be cos 30°, 1/2 scored.

$R(\uparrow)$, $R + P\sin 30° - 50g = 0$

Error here – should be $-P\sin 30°$, 2/3 scored.

From (1), $R = P$

So, $P + \frac{1}{2}P = 50g$

$\frac{3P}{2} = 50g$

$P = \frac{100g}{3}$

$= \frac{980}{3}$

$= 326\frac{2}{3}$

Candidate correctly solves his/her equations to give a value of *P* (incorrect due to error earlier), 2/4 scored.

Resolving forces is a key skill in Mechanics and candidates must be able to do it quickly and correctly.

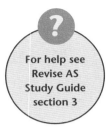

(2) A truck T of mass 2 tonnes is travelling due east along a straight horizontal track with constant speed 12 m s^{-1}. The truck T collides with another truck S which is travelling due west along the same track as T with constant speed 6 m s^{-1}. The magnitude of the impulse in the collision is $28\,000 \text{ N s}$. [1 tonne = 1000 kg].

(a) Find the speed of T immediately after the collision. [3]

A good clear diagram showing **all** the information.

For T: using $I = mv - mu \; (\rightarrow +ve)$

$-28\,800 \quad = 2000\,(-v) - 2000 \times 12$

$\Rightarrow 2000v \quad = 4800$

$\Rightarrow v = 2.4$

Correct equation.

Correct answer, 3/3 scored.

(b) State the direction in which T moves after the collision. [1]

Since $v > 0$, T moves due west.

Correct, 1/1 scored.

Immediately after the collision the speed of S is 3.6 m s^{-1}, and S and T are moving in opposite directions.

(c) Find the mass of S. [4]

So, $w = 3.6$ (see diagram)

For S: Using $I = mv - mu \; (\rightarrow +ve)$

$28\,000 = m(6 - 3.6)$

$\Rightarrow m = 12\,000\,g$

Sign error here should be $m(3.6 - -6)$ i.e. $m(3.6 + 6)$ giving $m = 3000$, **2/4 scored**.

Exam practice questions

3.1 Kinematics

1 A cricket ball is thrown vertically upwards from ground level with speed u m s^{-1} and takes 4 s to reach the ground again. Neglecting air resistance,

   (a) draw a velocity–time graph to represent the motion of the ball during the first 4 s, [2]

   (b) find the maximum height of the ball above the ground. [6]

2 A lorry accelerates along a straight horizontal road from a speed of 14 m s^{-1} to a speed of 34 m s^{-1} in 20 s.

   (a) Find how far the lorry travels during this 20 s period. [2]

   (b) Find how long it takes to cover half of this distance. [7]

3 A stone is dropped from the top of a building of height h and hits the ground t seconds later. Neglecting air resistance,

   (a) write down an equation relating h and t. [2]

One second later another stone is thrown vertically downwards from the top of the same building with a speed of 19.6 m s^{-1}. Given that the two stones strike the ground at the same time and neglecting air resistance,

   (b) write down another equation relating h and t. [2]

   (c) Find the height of the building. [4]

4 A vertical wall is 33 m high. A ball is thrown vertically upwards from a point on ground level close to the wall with an initial speed of 25.9 m s^{-1}. Find for how long the ball will be above the top of the wall. [7]

3.2 Moments

1 A uniform beam AB of mass 20 kg and length 2.4 m is at rest in equilibrium in a horizontal position. The beam is supported by two vertical ropes XP and YQ attached to the beam at the points P and Q where $AP = 0.4$ m and $QB = 0.6$ m. Find

   (a) the tension in XP, [4]

   (b) the tension in YQ. [2]

Answers on pages 50–59 Answers on pages 50–59 Answers on pages 50–59

2 A uniform rod AE, of length 0.8 m and mass 2 kg, rests horizontally on two smooth supports placed at B and D. Given that $AB = 0.1$ m and $DE = 0.2$ m, find

    (a) the thrust on the support at B,   [3]

    (b) the thrust on the support at D.   [2]

When a load of mass M kg is attached to the rod at the point A, the rod is about to tilt about the point B. When the load of mass M kg is attached to the rod at a point x cm from E, the rod is about to tilt about the point D. Find the value of

    (c) M,   [5]

    (d) x.   [3]

3 A non-uniform rod ABC of length 12 m and mass 60 kg has its centre of mass at G where $AG = 5$ m. Three light strings are attached to the rod at A, B and C where $AB = 8$ m. The rod is at rest in equilibrium with the three strings vertical.

    (a) Given that the tension in the string attached at B has magnitude 25 g, find the magnitudes of the tensions in the other two strings.   [4]

    (b) Find how far the point B would have to be moved in order for the magnitudes of the tensions in all three strings to be the same.   [4]

3.3 Statics

1 A particle is suspended by two light inextensible strings and hangs in equilibrium. The first string is inclined at 60° to the horizontal and the tension in that string is 30 N and the second string is inclined at 30° to the horizontal. Find, to 3 significant figures,

    (a) the weight of the particle,   [3]

    (b) the tension in the second string.   [3]

2 A particle is placed on a rough plane inclined at an angle α to the horizontal, where $\tan\alpha = \frac{3}{4}$. The particle is maintained in equilibrium by a horizontal force of magnitude 20 N which acts in the vertical plane containing the line of greatest slope of the inclined plane through the particle. The coefficient of friction between the particle and the plane is $\frac{1}{2}$. Given that the particle is on the point of slipping up the plane,

    (a) find the normal reaction of the plane on the particle,   [4]

    (b) the weight of the particle.   [3]

3 A body of mass M kg is supported in equilibrium by two ropes attached to it. One rope is inclined at 30° to the vertical and the other at 60° to the vertical. The body is modelled as a particle and the ropes are modelled as being light and inextensible. Given that either rope breaks if the tension in it exceeds 4900 N, find, to 3 significant figures, the greatest possible value of M.   [7]

4 A block of mass 4 kg is placed on a plane inclined at an angle of 30° to the horizontal. The coefficient of friction between the block and the plane is 0.2.

(a) Show that the block will slide down the plane. [4]

(b) Find the magnitude of the *least horizontal* force that is needed to prevent it sliding down the plane. [7]

3.4 Vectors

1 Two constant forces $\mathbf{F}_1$ and $\mathbf{F}_2$ are given by $\mathbf{F}_1 = (2\mathbf{i} - 6\mathbf{j})$ N and $\mathbf{F}_2 = (a\mathbf{i} + 2a\mathbf{j})$ N.

(a) Find the angle between $\mathbf{F}_1$ and $\mathbf{i}$. [3]

The resultant $\mathbf{R}$ of $\mathbf{F}_1$ and $\mathbf{F}_2$ is parallel to $\mathbf{j}$.

(b) Find the magnitude of $\mathbf{R}$. [4]

2 [*In this question, the horizontal unit vectors* $\mathbf{i}$ *and* $\mathbf{j}$ *are directed due east and due north respectively.*]

At 3 pm cyclist C has position vector $(-9\mathbf{i} + 6\mathbf{j})$ km and is moving with constant velocity $(3\mathbf{i} + 12\mathbf{j})$ km h^{-1} and cyclist D has position vector $(16\mathbf{i} + 6\mathbf{j})$ km and is moving with constant velocity $(-9\mathbf{i} + 3\mathbf{j})$ km h^{-1}.

(a) Find how far apart the cyclists are at 3 pm. [1]

(b) Write down the position vectors of C and D after a further t hours. [3]

(c) Hence find the vector from C to D after a further t hours. [2]

(d) At what time will C be due north of D? [3]

3 A particle P of mass 2.5 kg moves under the action of a single constant force $\mathbf{F}$. At time $t = 0$ the velocity of P is $(-2\mathbf{i} + \mathbf{j})$ m s^{-1} and 2 seconds later its velocity is $(4\mathbf{i} - 7\mathbf{j})$ m s^{-1}.

(a) Find, in vector form, the acceleration of P. [2]

(b) Find the magnitude of $\mathbf{F}$. [2]

(c) Find, to the nearest degree, the acute angle between the line of action of $\mathbf{F}$ and the line $y = x$. [4]

4 [*In this question, the horizontal unit vectors* $\mathbf{i}$ *and* $\mathbf{j}$ *are directed due east and due north respectively.*]

The velocity of a particle P at time t seconds is modelled by the formula

$\mathbf{v} = (3t^2 + 1)\mathbf{i} + (7t - 1)\mathbf{j}$ m s^{-1}.

(a) Find the direction of motion of P after 2 seconds. [3]

(b) At what time is P first moving parallel to the vector $\mathbf{i} + \mathbf{j}$? [6]

3.5 Momentum and impulse

1 A bullet of mass 100 g is fired into a wooden block of mass 4.9 kg which lies at rest on a rough horizontal floor. The bullet enters the block horizontally at $300\,\text{m s}^{-1}$ and becomes embedded in it.

(a) Find the initial speed of the block. [3]

The block slides along the floor eventually coming to rest. Given that the coefficient of friction between the floor and the block is 0.5,

(b) find, to 2 significant figures, how far the block slides. [6]

2 A cannon of mass 600 kg lies at rest on a rough horizontal plane. It is used to fire a 2 kg shell horizontally with an initial speed of $300\,\text{m s}^{-1}$.

(a) Find the magnitude of the impulse exerted on the shell by the cannon. [2]

(b) Find the initial speed of recoil of the cannon. [2]

Given that the cannon travels a distance of 10.2 cm before coming to rest,

(c) find, to 1 decimal place, the coefficient of friction between the cannon and the plane. [6]

3 A particle A of mass $2m$ is moving on a smooth horizontal floor with speed u. Another particle B of mass km is moving on the floor with speed $3u$ in the opposite direction. The two particles collide directly and as a result of the collision the direction of motion of both particles is reversed and the speed of A is halved. Find

(a) the range of possible values of k, [5]

(b) the magnitude of the impulse on A from B. [3]

4 A particle P of mass $2m$ and a particle Q of mass $3m$ are attached to the ends of a light inextensible string. The particles are at rest and next to each other on a smooth horizontal plane with the string slack. Particle P is then projected along the plane directly away from Q with a speed $2u$.

(a) Find the speed of Q immediately after the string goes taut. [3]

(b) Explain how in your calculation you have used the modelling assumptions that the string is

    (i) light,   (ii) inextensible. [2]

(c) Find the impulse transmitted through the string as the string goes taut. [3]

Answers on pages 50–59 Answers on pages 50–59 Answers on pages 50–59

3.6 Dynamics

1 A particle of mass 2 kg is at rest on a rough horizontal plane. The coefficient of friction between the particle and the plane is $\frac{1}{4}$. A horizontal force of 18 N is applied to the body for 4 s and is then removed. Find

(a) the speed of the particle after 4 s, [5]

(b) the total distance travelled by the body in coming to rest. [7]

2

A particle A of mass 3m is at rest on a rough horizontal table. The particle is attached to one end of a light inextensible string which passes over a small smooth fixed pulley P which is at the edge of the table. Another particle B of mass 2m is attached to the other end of the string and hangs freely. The line AP is perpendicular to the edge of the table and A, P and B all lie in the same vertical plane. The system is released from rest with the string taut when A is 1.1 m from the edge of the table and B is 1 m from the floor, as shown in the figure. Given that B hits the floor after 2 s and does not rebound,

(a) find the acceleration of A during the first 2 s of the motion, [2]

(b) find, to 2 decimal places, the coefficient of friction between A and the table. [9]

(c) Determine, by calculation, whether A reaches the pulley. [7]

3 A car of mass 900 kg tows a caravan of mass 600 kg along a straight horizontal road by means of a light rigid tow bar. The resistance to motion is proportional to mass. Given that the caravan experiences a resistance of 200 N,

(a) find the resistance experienced by the car. [2]

Given that the acceleration of the system is $\frac{2}{3}$ m s^{-2}, find

(b) the tractive force provided by the engine of the car, [3]

(c) the tension in the tow bar. [3]

When the speed of the car is 16 m s^{-1} the driver sees a hazard ahead and applies the brakes to bring the car to rest. Given that the overall braking force is 1500 N and that the resistance to the motion of the car and caravan remains the same as before,

(d) find the distance travelled by the car in coming to rest, [5]

(e) determine the magnitude and nature of the force in the tow bar during the braking period. [4]

Answers on pages 50–59 Answers on pages 50–59 Answers on pages 50–59

Answers

3.1 Kinematics

(1) (a)

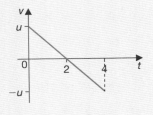

Since this is a velocity–time graph, we need a positive direction (upwards).

(b) Gradient of graph $= -9.8$

So, $-\dfrac{u}{2} = -9.8$

$\Rightarrow \quad u = 19.6$

Height = Area under graph between $t = 0$ and $t = 2$

$\qquad = \frac{1}{2} \times 2 \times 19.6$

$\qquad = 19.6 \, \text{m}$

Or use the constant acceleration formulae.
This is an important result.

(2) (a) $s = \left(\dfrac{u + v}{2}\right)t$

$\qquad = \left(\dfrac{14 + 34}{2}\right) \times 20$

$\qquad = 480 \, \text{m}$

It may be useful to write down which of s, u, v, c, a you know and which you are trying to find.

(b) Half distance $= 240 \, \text{m}$

$s = ut + \frac{1}{2}at^2$

$240 = 14t + \frac{1}{2}at^2$

where $a = \dfrac{v - u}{t} = \dfrac{34 - 14}{20} = 1 \, \text{m s}^{-2}$

Hence, $240 = 14t + \frac{1}{2}t^2$

$\Rightarrow t^2 + 28t - 480 = 0$

$\Rightarrow (t + 40)(t - 12) = 0$

$\Rightarrow t = -40$ or $t = 12$

Hence, it takes 12 seconds.

We cannot use a formula which has v in it.
From: $v = u + at$.

Use the quadratic formulae if you can't factorise.

(3) (a) $s = ut + \frac{1}{2}at^2 \; (\downarrow)$

$h = \frac{1}{2}gt^2$ $\qquad\qquad$ (1)

$(\downarrow)$ indicates downwards is the positive direction.

(b) $s = ut + \frac{1}{2}at^2 \; (\downarrow)$

$h = 19.6(t - 1) + \frac{1}{2}g(t - 1)^2$ $\quad$ (2)

This stone is in the air for 1 second less hence: $(t - 1)$.

(c) Hence,

$\frac{1}{2}gt^2 = 19.6t - 19.6 + \frac{1}{2}g(t^2 - 2t + 1)$

$0 = 19.6t - 19.6 - 9.8t + 4.9$

$14.7 = 9.8t$

$1.5 = t$

Hence, $h = \frac{1}{2} \times 9.8 \times 1.5^2$

$\qquad = 11 \, \text{m}$ (2 s.f.)

Cancel $\frac{1}{2}gt^2$.
Use $g = 9.8$.

Since we have used $g = 9.8$, the final answer should be given to 2 s.f.

(4) $s = ut + \frac{1}{2}at^2$ ($\uparrow$)

$33 = 25.9t - \frac{1}{2} \times 9.8t^2$

$\Rightarrow 4.9t^2 - 25.9t + 33 = 0$

$t = \dfrac{25.9 \pm \sqrt{25.9^2 - 4 \times 4.9 \times 33}}{9.8}$

$t = \dfrac{25.9 \pm 4.9}{9.8}$

$t = \dfrac{21}{9.8}$ or $\dfrac{30.8}{9.8}$

Ball is above top of wall for $\dfrac{30.8 - 21}{9.8} = 1$ second.

> This equation will give the two times when the ball is 33 m above the ground.

> We need the difference between these two times.

3.2 Moments

(1) (a)

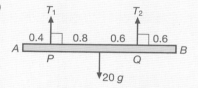

$M(P),\ 20g \times 0.8 = T_2 \times 1.4$

$\Rightarrow \qquad\qquad T_2 = 112\,\text{N}$

> A clear force diagram is essential. A common error is to omit the *weight* of the beam.

(b) $R(\uparrow),\ T_1 + T_2 = 20g$

$\Rightarrow \qquad T_1 = 196 - 112$

$= 84\,\text{N}$

> OR: Take moments about Q.

(2) (a)

$M(D),\ 2g \times 0.2 = 0.5T_1$

$\Rightarrow \qquad\qquad T_1 = 0.8g$

$= 7.8\,\text{N (2 s.f.)}$

Hence, by Newton's 3rd law, the thrust on B will also be 7.8 N.

> Show all the forces and lengths on your diagram.

(b) $R(\uparrow),\ T_1 + T_2 = 2g$

$\Rightarrow \qquad T_2 = 1.2g = 11.8\,\text{N (3 s.f.)}$

> OR: Take moments about B.

(c)

$M(B),\ Mg \times 0.1 = 2g \times 0.3$

$M = 6$

> When the rod is about to tilt about B, there will be a zero contact force at D.

(d)

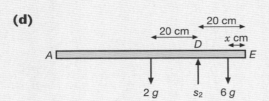

$M(D),\ 2g \times 20 = 6g \times (20 - x)$

$\qquad\quad 40 = 120 - 6x$

$\qquad\quad 6x = 80$

$\qquad\quad x = \frac{40}{3} = 13\frac{1}{3}$

Since we have x cm, we need to mark in cm on both sides of the equation.

(3) (a)

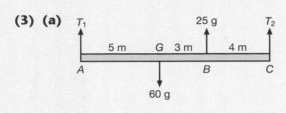

A non-uniform rod does not have its centre of mass at its midpoint. A clear force diagram is essential.

$M(A),\ (60g \times 5) = (25g \times 8) + (T_2 \times 12)$

$\Rightarrow \qquad 300g = 200g + 12T_2$

$\Rightarrow \qquad 100g = 12T_2$

$\Rightarrow \qquad \frac{25g}{3} = T_2 (81\frac{2}{3}\,\text{N})$

Try to take moments about a point through which an unknown force passes.

$R(\uparrow),\ T_1 + T_2 = 60g - 25g$

$\Rightarrow \qquad T_1 = 35g - T_2$

$\qquad\qquad = 35g - \frac{25g}{3}$

$\qquad\qquad = \frac{105g - 25g}{3}$

$\qquad\qquad = \frac{80g}{3}\ (261\frac{1}{3}\,\text{N})$

When tackling problems on bodies in equilibrium, which involve taking moments, don't forget about resolving.

(b)

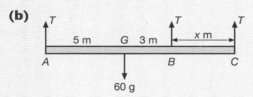

Suppose B is a distance x m from C.

$R(\uparrow),\ 3T = 60g \Rightarrow T = 20g$

$M(C),\ 60g \times 7 = 20g \times x + 20g \times 12$

$\qquad\quad 21 = x + 12$

$\qquad\quad 9 = x$

So, B needs to be 2 m to the left of G
i.e. B needs to be moved 5 m.

Divide through by $20g$.

3.3 Statics

(1) (a)

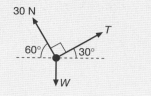

$R(\nwarrow)$, $30 = W\cos30°$

$\Rightarrow \quad 30 = W\dfrac{\sqrt{3}}{2}$

$\Rightarrow \quad \dfrac{60}{\sqrt{3}} = W$

$\Rightarrow 20\sqrt{3} = W$

> Clearly the strings must be at right angles to each other; this can be exploited to make the solution easier: by resolving along the first string, we do not get T in our equation.

(b) $R(\nearrow)$, $T = W\cos60°$
$= 20\sqrt{3} \times \frac{1}{2}$
$= 10\sqrt{3}\,\text{N}$

> Similarly, by resolving along the second string, we get a simple solution.

Alternative:

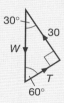

Draw a △ of forces: using SOHCAHTOA,
$W\sin60° = 30$

$\tan30° = \dfrac{T}{30}$

etc.

> A more routine solution can be obtained by resolving horizontally and vertically.

(2) (a)

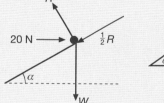 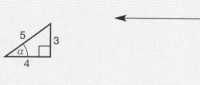

> Since the particle is on the point of slipping **up the plane**, friction will be limiting acting **down the plane**.

$R(\rightarrow)$, $20 = R\sin\alpha + \frac{1}{2}R\cos\alpha$
$\Rightarrow \quad 20 = (R \cdot \frac{3}{5}) + \frac{1}{2} \times (R \times \frac{4}{5})$
$\Rightarrow \quad 20 = R$

> Using the triangle above $(3, 4, 5\triangle)$.

(b) $R(\uparrow)$, $R\cos\alpha = W + \frac{1}{2}R\sin\alpha$
$(20 \times \frac{4}{5}) = W + (\frac{1}{2} \times 20 \times \frac{3}{5})$
$10 = W$

> Other solutions may involve resolving parallel and/or perpendicular to the plane.

(3)

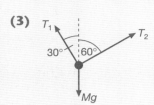

$R(\rightarrow)$, $T_2\cos30° = T_1\sin30°$ ⟵ We must decide which of T_1 and T_2 is greater.

$\Rightarrow \quad T_2 \cdot \dfrac{\sqrt{3}}{2} = T_1 \cdot \dfrac{1}{2}$

i.e. $T_1 > T_2$

Hence, T_1 will reach the maximum tension of 4900 N first.

$R(\nwarrow)$, $4900 = Mg\cos30°$ ⟵ Now resolve along the string.

$\Rightarrow \quad 500 = M\dfrac{\sqrt{3}}{2}$

$\Rightarrow \dfrac{1000\sqrt{3}}{3} = M$

(4) (a)

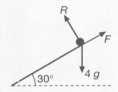

$R(\nwarrow)$, $R = 4g\cos30°$

$\qquad = 4g\dfrac{\sqrt{3}}{2}$

$\qquad = 2g\sqrt{3}$

$\Rightarrow$ Maximum friction $= 2g\sqrt{3} \times 0.2$ ⟵ We need to find the value of the maximum friction force i.e. μR.

$\qquad\qquad\qquad = 0.4g\sqrt{3} \simeq 0.693g$

Component of weight down the plane in $4g\cos60° = 2g$ ⟵ We can compare it with the

Since $2g > 0.693g$, the block slides down the plane. weight component down the plane.

(b)

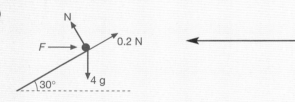

⟵ When F is at its *least* possible value, the block will be on the point of slipping *down* the plane; hence friction will be limiting and acting *up* the plane.

$R(\uparrow)$, $N\cos30° + 0.2\,N\cos60° = 4g$

$\Rightarrow N = \dfrac{4g}{(\cos30° + 0.1)}$

$\qquad = 40.579$

$R(\rightarrow)$, $F + 0.2\,N\cos30° = N\cos60°$

$\Rightarrow F = N(0.5 - 0.2\cos30°)$

$\qquad \simeq 40.579\,(0.5 - 0.2\cos30°)$

$\qquad = 13.3\,\text{N (3 s.f.)}$

3.4 Vectors

(1) (a)

$$\tan\theta = \tfrac{6}{2} = 3$$
$$\Rightarrow \theta = 71.6°$$

A simple diagram is useful.

(b) $\mathbf{R} = \mathbf{F}_1 + \mathbf{F}_2$

$\quad = (2\mathbf{i} - 6\mathbf{j}) + (a\mathbf{i} + 2a\mathbf{j})$

$\quad = (2 + a)\mathbf{i} + (2a - 6)\mathbf{j}$

So, $(2 + a) = 0$

$\Rightarrow \qquad a = -2$

$\mathbf{R} = -10\mathbf{j} \Rightarrow |\mathbf{R}| = 10$

Since R is parallel to $\mathbf{j}$ the $\mathbf{i}$ component $= 0$.

(2) (a) $\overrightarrow{CD} = \overrightarrow{CO} + \overrightarrow{OD}$

$\quad = 9\mathbf{i} - 6\mathbf{j} + 16\mathbf{i} + 6\mathbf{j}$

$\quad = 25\mathbf{i}$

$\therefore CD = |25\mathbf{i}| = 25$ km

Using the triangle law.

(b) $\mathbf{r}_C = -9\mathbf{i} + 6\mathbf{j} + t(3\mathbf{i} + 12\mathbf{j})$

$\mathbf{r}_D = 16\mathbf{i} + 6\mathbf{j} + t(-9\mathbf{i} + 3\mathbf{j})$

Initial p.v. $+ (t \times$ velocity).

(c) $\overrightarrow{CD} = -\mathbf{r}_C + \mathbf{r}_D$

$\quad = 25\mathbf{i} + t(-12\mathbf{i} - 9\mathbf{j})$

$\quad = (25 - 12t)\mathbf{i} - 9t\mathbf{j}$

Collecting the components.

(d) C will be due N of D when

$25 - 12t = 0$

$t = \dfrac{25}{12}$ h

$\quad = 2$ h 5 min

i.e. at 5.05 pm.

Since $\mathbf{i}$ is due E, the $\mathbf{i}$ component must be zero.

(3) (a) $\mathbf{a} = \dfrac{\mathbf{v} - \mathbf{u}}{t}$

$\quad = \dfrac{(4\mathbf{i} - 7\mathbf{j}) - (-2\mathbf{i} + \mathbf{j})}{2}$

$\quad = \dfrac{6\mathbf{i} - 8\mathbf{j}}{2}$

$\quad = 3\mathbf{i} - 4\mathbf{j}$

i.e. $\mathbf{a} = (3\mathbf{i} - 4\mathbf{j})\,\mathrm{m\,s^{-2}}$

This is the vector version of $v = u + at$.
The second pair of brackets are essential.

(b) $|\mathbf{a}| = \sqrt{3^2 + (-4)^2} = 5$

So, $|\mathbf{F}| = m|\mathbf{a}| = 2.5 \times 5$

$\quad = 12.5$ N

Alternatively, we could use $\mathbf{F} = m\mathbf{a}$ first, then find its magnitude.

(c) Since, $\mathbf{F} = m\mathbf{a}$, the direction of $\mathbf{F}$ is the same as the direction of $\mathbf{a}$.

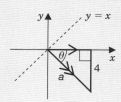

$\tan\theta = \dfrac{4}{3}$

$\Rightarrow \theta = 53°$ (nearest degree)

$\therefore$ Required angle

$\quad = 180° - (53° + 45°)$

$\quad = 82°$

A simple diagram is essential.

(4) (a) When $t = 2$, $\mathbf{v} = 13\mathbf{i} + 13\mathbf{j}$

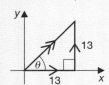

$\tan\theta = \frac{13}{13} = 1 \Rightarrow \theta = 45°$

i.e. P is moving at 45° to the x-axis i.e. NE.

> Direction of motion is given by the direction of **v**.

(b) P will be moving parallel to $\mathbf{i} + \mathbf{j}$ when the $\mathbf{i}$ component = $\mathbf{j}$ component

i.e. $3t^2 + 1 = 7t - 1$

$\Rightarrow 3t^2 - 7t + 2 = 0$

$\Rightarrow (3t - 1)(t - 2) = 0$

$\Rightarrow t = \frac{1}{3}$ or 2

Hence, **first** time is after $\frac{1}{3}$ second.

> Alternatively, use the quadratic formula.
> We need the smaller of the two solutions.

3.5 Momentum and impulse

(1) (a)

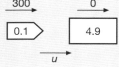

Conservation of momentum:

$300 \times 0.1 = 5u$

$30 = 5u$

$6 = u$

> A clear diagram, with arrows, showing initial and final velocities is essential.

(b)

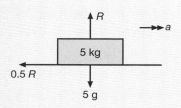

> Friction will be limiting since the block is sliding.

$R(\uparrow)$, $R = 5g$

$R(\rightarrow)$, $-0.5R = 5a$

$\Rightarrow -0.1 \times 5g = a$

$\Rightarrow \qquad -0.5g = a$

$v^2 = u^2 + 2as$

$0^2 = 6^2 + 2(-0.5g)s$

$\Rightarrow s = 3.7\,\text{m}$ (2 s.f.)

> First we find the deceleration of the block.

> 2 s.f. answer as we've used $g = 9.8$.

(2) (a)

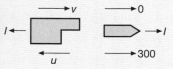

> Using $I = m(v - u)$.

For shell: $I = 2(300 - 0) = 600\,\text{N s}$.

(b) Conservation of momentum:

$0 = 300 \times 2 - 600u$

$\Rightarrow u = 1$

Mechanics 1

(c) $R(\rightarrow)$, $-\mu 600g = 600a$ ← First find the acceleration.

$v^2 = u^2 + 2as$: $0^2 = 1^2 + 2(-\mu g) \times 0.102$

$\Rightarrow \mu = \dfrac{1}{2g \times 0.102} = 0.5$ (1 d.p.)

(3) (a)

It's a good idea, in questions where the impulse is required, to put the impulses on the diagram.

CLM: $2mu - km \cdot 3u = kmv - 2m \cdot \dfrac{u}{2}$

$2mu - 3kmu = kmv - mu$

$\dfrac{3u - 3ku}{k} = v$

i.e. $\dfrac{3u}{k}(1-k) = v$

but $v > 0$ ← We are told that B rebounds.

i.e. $\dfrac{3u}{k}(1-k) > 0$

$1 - k > 0$ ← Divide both sides by $3\dfrac{u}{k}$ (>0).

$1 > k$

(b) For A: $(\leftarrow)$ ← The arrow indicates the positive direction.

$I = 2m(\dfrac{u}{2} - -u)$

$= 3mu$ ← This is the magnitude of the impulse of B on A.

(4) (a)

Draw the diagram just before the string goes taut.

CLM: $4mu = 2mv + 3mv$

$0.8u = v$

(b) (i) Ignored the momentum of the string.

(ii) Assumed both P and Q have the same speed immediately after the string goes tight. ← This is a crucial assumption without which the problem would be insoluble.

(c) For Q: $(\leftarrow)$: $I = 3mv$

$= 3m \times 0.8u$

$= 2.4mu$

Mechanics 1

57

3.6 Dynamics

(1) (a)

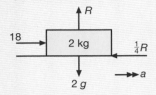

A simple diagram showing all the (relevant) forces **and** the acceleration is essential.

$R(\uparrow)$, $R = 2g = 19.6N$

$R(\rightarrow)$, $18 - \frac{1}{4} \times 19.6 = 2a$ ①

$\qquad\qquad 6.55 = a$

Always resolve in the direction of the acceleration.

$v = u + at$:

Since a is constant, we can use *suvat* formulae.

$v = 0 + 6.55 \times 4$

$\quad = 26.2 \, \text{m s}^{-1}$

(b) $R(\rightarrow)$, $-\frac{1}{4} \times 19.6 = 2a$

This is the same equation as ① above, without the 18 N force.

$\Rightarrow a = -2.45$

$v^2 = u^2 + 2as$

$0^2 = 26.2^2 + 2 \times (-2.45)s$

$\Rightarrow s = \dfrac{26.2^2}{4.9} = 140 \, \text{m (3 s.f.)}$

This is the distance travelled in coming to rest from a speed of $26.2 \, \text{m s}^{-1}$.

$s = \dfrac{(u+v)}{2}t$

We now find how far it travelled in the first 4 seconds.

$s = \dfrac{(26.2 + 0)}{2} . 4$

$\quad = 52.4 \, \text{m}$

$\therefore$ Total distance $= 52.4 + 140.09$

$\qquad\qquad\qquad = 192 \, \text{m (3 s.f.)}$

(2) (a)

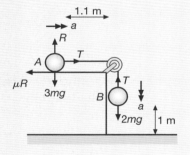

A good diagram, showing all the forces **and** the accelerations is essential.

$s = ut + \frac{1}{2}at^2 (\downarrow)$ for B

$1 = 0 + \frac{1}{2}a . 2^2$

$\Rightarrow a = \frac{1}{2} \text{m s}^{-2}$

Hence, the acceleration of A is $\frac{1}{2}\text{m s}^{-2}$

This is true because the string is inextensible.

(b) For A: $R(\uparrow)$, $R = 3mg$

No acceleration vertically.

$R(\rightarrow)$, $T - \mu . 3mg = 3m \times \frac{1}{2}$ ①

Resolving in the direction of 'a'.

For B: $R(\downarrow)$, $2mg - T = 2m \times \frac{1}{2}$ ②

Adding ① and ②:

This is always the easiest way of eliminating T.

$2\not{m}g - 3\mu\not{m}g = \dfrac{5\not{m}}{2}$

$\Rightarrow \quad 4g - 5 = 6\mu g$

Since we are using $g = 9.8$ answers should be given to 2 s.f. accuracy.

$\Rightarrow \qquad \mu = \dfrac{4g - 5}{6g}$

$\qquad\qquad = 0.58 \, \text{(2 d.p.)}$

Mechanics 1

(c) Let v be the speed of A when B hits the floor. Then, using
$v = u + at$ $(\rightarrow)$, for A
$v = \frac{1}{2} \times 2 = 1\,\text{m s}^{-1}$
When B hits the floor, A will continue to slide along the table with the string slack – so put $T = 0$ in equation ① above to find the deceleration of A, a':
$\mu \cdot \cancel{3}\cancel{m}g = \cancel{3}\cancel{m}a'$
$\Rightarrow \left(\dfrac{4g - 5}{6\cancel{g}}\right) \cdot \cancel{g} = a'$
$\Rightarrow \qquad\qquad 5.7 = a'$
use $v^2 = u^2 + 2as$ $(\rightarrow)$ for A
$0^2 = 1^2 - 2 \times 5.7 \times s$
$\Rightarrow s = \frac{1}{11.4} = 0.0877$
Since $s < 0.1$, A will **not** reach the pulley.

Note that v will also be the speed of B when it hits the floor.

A common error is to use m for the mass (instead of $3m$).

s is the distance that A will slide before it comes to rest.

Note that A will be 0.1 m from the pulley when B hits the floor.

(3) (a)

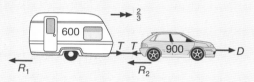

D is the driving force of the engine of the car.

$R_1 = 200$ and $R_1 \propto$ mass
i.e. $R_1 = 600k$
$\Rightarrow 200 = 600k$
$\Rightarrow \quad k = \frac{1}{3}$
So, $R_2 = \frac{1}{3} \times 900 = 300\,\text{N}$

An alternative method would be:
$\dfrac{R_2}{R_1} = \dfrac{900}{600} = \dfrac{3}{2}$
$\Rightarrow R_2 = \dfrac{3}{2} \times 200 = 300\,\text{N}$

(b) For the whole system: $R(\rightarrow)$,
$D - 200 - 300 = 1500 \times \frac{2}{3}$
$\Rightarrow \qquad\qquad D = 1500\,\text{N}$

(c) For caravan: $R(\rightarrow)$,
$T - 200 = 600 \times \frac{2}{3}$
$\Rightarrow \quad T = 600\,\text{N}$

If we consider either the car or caravan **separately**, the unknown T will appear in the equation.

OR: For car: $R(\rightarrow)$,
$1500 - 300 - T = 900 \times \dfrac{2}{3}$
$\Rightarrow T \quad = 600\,\text{N}$

(d) For whole system: $R(\rightarrow)$,
$-1500 - 200 - 300 = 1500a$
$\Rightarrow \qquad\qquad\qquad a = -\frac{4}{3}$
$v^2 = u^2 + 2as$ $(\rightarrow)$
$0^2 = 16^2 + 2 \times (-\frac{4}{3}) \times s$
$\Rightarrow s = 96\,\text{m}$

a is the new acceleration which will of course be negative.

(e) For caravan:

T' will be the compression force in the towbar under braking.

$R(\rightarrow)$, $-200 - T' = 600 \times -\frac{4}{3}$
$\qquad\qquad 200 + T' = 800$
$\qquad\qquad\qquad T' = 600\,\text{N}$ (a compression).

Mechanics 1

Chapter 4

Statistics 1

Questions with model answers

C grade candidate – mark scored 6/10

Examiner's Commentary

(1) A fair six-sided die is rolled. The random variable S represents the score on the uppermost face.

(?) For help see Revise AS Study Guide section 4

(a) Write down the probability function of S. **[2]**

$$P(S = s) = \frac{1}{6} \qquad s = 1, 2, 3, 4, 5, 6$$

All correct, **2/2 scored.**

(b) Find the value of $E(6S + 2)$. **[4]**

$$E(S) = \frac{6 + 1}{2} = 3.5$$

Correct – by symmetry.

$$E(6S + 2) = 6 \times 3.5 = 21$$

Incorrect – candidate has forgotten to add 2. **2/4 scored.**

(c) Find the value of $\text{Var}(4S - 2)$. **[4]**

$$\text{Var}(S) = \frac{6^2 - 1}{12} = \frac{35}{12}$$

Correct – quoting the formula $\frac{n^2 - 1}{12}$ for the variance of the discrete uniform distribution.

$$\text{Var}(4S - 2) = 4 \times \frac{35}{12}$$

$$= \frac{35}{3}$$

Incorrect – candidate has forgotten to square the 4:
$\text{Var}(4S - 2)$
$= 4^2\text{Var}(S)$
2/4 scored.

Learn the results: $\quad E(aX + b) = aE(X) + b$
$$\text{Var}(aX + b) = a^2\text{Var}(X)$$
for a discrete random variable X.

A grade candidate – mark scored 6/8

For help see Revise AS Study Guide section 4

(2) The random variable Y is normally distributed with mean 177.0 and standard deviation 6.4.

(a) Find $P(166 \leqslant Y \leqslant 185)$. [4]

$$P(166 \leqslant Y \leqslant 185) = P(\frac{166 - 177}{6.4} \leqslant Z \leqslant \frac{185 - 177}{6.4})$$

$$= P(-1.72 \leqslant Z \leqslant 1.25)$$

$$= \Phi(1.25) - \Phi(-1.72)$$

$$= \Phi(1.25) - (1 - \Phi(1.72))$$

$$= 0.8517$$

All correct, 4/4 scored.

It is proposed that Y might be a suitable random variable to model the height, in cm, of adult males.

(b) Give two reasons why this is a sensible proposal. [2]

Height is a continuous random variable.

1/2 scored.

Other reasons could be: male heights cluster round a central value of approx. 1.77 m. Most male heights are within the range $177\,cm \pm (3 \times 6.4\,cm)$.

Note that: if there are *2 marks* available give *2 reasons*.

(c) Explain briefly how mathematical models can help to improve our understanding of real-world problems. [2]

A model simplifies the problem and allows us to make predications.

1/2 scored.

A model will be quicker and easier and cheaper to use.

Statistics 1

4.1 Summarising and representing data

Statistics 1

1 The times, in minutes, taken by 100 competitors to complete a certain task are summarised in the table below:

Time	No. of competitors
30–39	4
40–44	13
45–49	32
50–54	21
55–59	12
60–69	10
70–99	8

(a) Estimate, using linear interpolation, the median and interquartile range for these data. [5]
The shortest time taken is 30 minutes and the longest time is 98 minutes.

(b) Represent these data using a boxplot. [4]

The data is coded using $x = \dfrac{t - 52}{5}$, where t represents the mid-point of each group.

This gives the following: $\Sigma fx = 17$ and $\Sigma fx^2 = 545.5$.

(c) Estimate, using these values, the mean and standard deviation of the times taken to complete the task. [6]

(d) Which summary statistics, median and IQR, or mean and standard deviation, would be most appropriate to use with these data? Give a reason for your answer. [2]

2 In a survey the times, t seconds, taken by 20 participants to do a number of simple calculations are summarised by $\Sigma t = 454$, $\Sigma t^2 = 13\,502$.

(a) Find the mean and standard deviation of the times. [4]

The survey is repeated and 24 new participants take part. The mean and variance of their times are 22.5 seconds and 72.0 seconds² respectively.

(b) Find the mean and standard deviation of the times for all 44 participants. [6]

3 The total rainfall in mm, to the nearest mm, in Haslemere in the month of April, for all years on record is summarised in the table below:

Rainfall	100–159	160–199	200–239	240–299	300–399
Frequency	20	48	36	23	13

The data are represented on a histogram. The bar representing the class 160–199 is 4 cm wide and 18 cm high. Find the dimensions of the bars representing the following classes:

(a) 200–239, [3]

(b) 240–299. [4]

4.2 Probability

1 The events A and B are such that

$$P(A) = 0.28, \ P(A \cup B) = 0.76 \ \text{and} \ P(A \cap B) = 0.17.$$

Find

(a) $P(A \cap B')$ [2]

(b) $P(B)$, [2]

(c) $P(A' \mid B')$. [4]

(d) Determine whether A and B are independent events. [2]

2 The events E and F are such that

$$P(E \mid F) = \tfrac{3}{4}, \ P(F \mid E) = \tfrac{3}{8} \ \text{and} \ P(E) = \tfrac{1}{2}.$$

(a) State, giving a reason, whether or not E and F are independent. [2]

Find

(b) $P(E \cap F)$, [2]

(c) $P(F \mid E')$ [2]

(d) $P(F)$, [2]

(e) $P(E \mid F')$. [4]

3 A football team have to play 3 games in the group stage of a cup competition. The probability that the team keeps a clean sheet in the first game is 0.5. The probability that the team keeps a clean sheet in any subsequent game is 0.6 if they kept a clean sheet in the previous game and 0.3 if they did not.

(a) Find the probability that the team keeps a clean sheet in all 3 games. [3]

(b) Find the probability that the team concedes a goal in just one of the 3 games. [4]

(c) Given that the team keeps a clean sheet in the 3rd game, find the probability that the team kept a clean sheet in the 2nd game. [6]

4 The table below shows the grades achieved in Mathematics by a group of students.

Grade	A	B	C
Male	7	9	4
Female	8	12	6

One student is chosen at random from the group. Find the probability that this student

(a) is male and achieved a grade B, [2]

(b) achieved a grade C, given that the student is female, [3]

(c) is female given that the student did not achieve a grade A, [2]

(d) achieves at least a grade B given that the student is male. [3]

4.3 Discrete random variables

1 The discrete random variable X has the probability function

$$P(X = x) = \begin{cases} k(x - 3), & x = 0, 1, 2, 3. \\ 0 & \text{otherwise.} \end{cases}$$

Find

(a) the value of k, [3]

(b) $E(X)$, [3]

(c) $E(3X - 2)$, [2]

(d) $Var(3X - 2)$. [6]

2 Given that the discrete random variable Y is such that

$$E(2X + 1) = 5 \text{ and } Var(2X + 1) = 2,$$

find

(a) $E(X)$, [3]

(b) $Var(X)$, [2]

(c) $E(X^2)$, [3]

(d) $E(X - 2)^2$. [5]

3 The discrete random variable S has the following probability distribution:

s	1	2	3	4	5	6	7	8
$P(S = s)$	0.1	0.1	0.05	0.2	0.15	0.05	0.15	a

Find

(a) the value of a, [2]

(b) $F(3.5)$, [1]

(c) $P(|S - 3| < 2)$, [2]

(d) $E(S)$, [2]

(e) $Var(S)$. [4]

4 Two unbiased cubical dice with sides numbered from 1 to 6 are rolled together.

The discrete random variable H is the higher value shown on either die.

(a) Show that $P(H = 3) = \frac{5}{36}$. [3]

(b) Show that H has a probability function of the form

$$P(H = h) = \begin{cases} ph + q, & h = 1, 2, 3, 4, 5, 6 \\ 0, & \text{otherwise.} \end{cases}$$

where p and q are numbers to be found. [6]

(c) Find the value of $E(3H - 2)$. [4]

4.4 Linear regression and correlation

1 The table below shows the latitude, $t°$N, and the average daily maximum temperature in August, $T°$C, for six large cities in the northern hemisphere.

t	14.0	15.9	33.0	40.2	51.3	59.6
T	42.1	38.4	32.0	30.9	22.3	22.0

(a) Plot a scatter diagram showing these data. [3]

The following summary statistics were calculated:

$\Sigma t = 214$, $\Sigma t^2 = 9337.7$, $\Sigma T = 187.7$ and $\Sigma tT = 5953.33$

(b) Find an equation of the regression line of T on t. [7]

(c) Interpret the gradient and intercept of your regression line. [2]

(d) Use your regression line to estimate the average daily maximum temperature in August in a city C at latitude 9°N. [2]

In fact the average daily maximum temperature in August in the city C is 20.3 °C.

(e) Suggest a possible reason for the large difference between this value and the value predicted by your regression line. [2]

2 An investor notices that the share price of the company CFC seems to closely follow the FTSE 100 share price index. He decides to investigate further by taking values for a 26-week period. The share price, £c, of the company CFC and the value, f, of the FTSE 100 share price index are recorded at the end of each of the 26 weeks. The values are then coded using $x = f - 4500$ and $y = c - 100$ and the following summary statistics are produced:

$$\Sigma x = 880, \ \Sigma x^2 = 1\,604\,848, \ \Sigma y = 76.62, \ \Sigma xy = 51\,665.56 \text{ and } \Sigma y^2 = 1867.81.$$

(a) Find the product moment correlation coefficient between f and c. [8]

(b) Explain how your answer to part **(a)** would support the calculation of a regression line of c on f for these data. [1]

(c) Find the equation of this regression line in the form $c = a + bf$. [6]

(d) Explain the meaning of your value of b. [1]

(e) Estimate the value of the share price of CFC when the FTSE 100 share price index has a value of 4800. [2]

(f) The investor decides to use the regression line to try to make predictions about future share price values of the company CFC. Comment on this idea. [1]

4.5 The Normal distribution

1 The weights of a random sample of parcels at a sorting office are summarised in the table below:

Weight (kg)	0–0.5	–1.0	–1.5	–2.0	–3.0	–5.0	–8.0
No. of parcels	8	21	23	19	8	3	2

(a) Estimate, using linear interpolation, the lower and upper quartiles for these data. [4]

It is suggested that the Normal distribution may be a suitable distribution to use to model the distribution of the weights of the parcels.

(b) Find the mean and standard deviation of the normal distribution which has the same lower and upper quartiles as those found in part **(a)**. [5]

The actual mean and standard deviation of the weights of the parcels in the sample are 1.50 kg and 1.12 kg respectively.

(c) Comment on the suggestion that these data may follow a normal distribution. [2]

2 The random variable Y is normally distributed with mean 31.8 and variance 6.7.

Find

(a) the value of y such that $P(Y > y) = 0.1867$, [4]

(b) the value of a such that $P(|Y - 31.8| < a) = 0.9356$. [5]

(c) Given that the value of Y is bigger than 30, find the probability that Y is less than 33. [5]

Answers

4.1 Summarising and representing data

(1) (a) Median, $Q_2 = 49.5 + \frac{1}{21} \times (54.5 - 49.5)$

$= 49.7$ (3 s.f.)

Lower Quartile, $Q_1 = 44.5 + \frac{8}{32}(49.5 - 44.5)$

$= 45.75 = 45.8$ (3 s.f.)

Upper Quartile, $Q_3 = 54.5 + \frac{5}{12}(59.5 - 54.5)$

$= 56.6$ (3 s.f.)

So, IQR $= Q_3 - Q_1 = 10.8$ (3 s.f.)

examiner's tips

For $N = 100$, the median can be taken as $(\frac{100}{2})$th figure i.e. 50th figure.

44.5 is the *lower class* boundary of the interval in which Q_1 lies.

Numerical answers should usually be given to 3 s.f.

(b)

30 40 50 60 70 80 90 100 (Time in minutes)

Boxplots should be done on graph paper; labels etc. must be included.

(c) $\bar{x} = \frac{\Sigma fx}{\Sigma f} = \frac{17}{100} = 0.17$;

$S_x = \sqrt{\frac{\Sigma fx^2}{\Sigma f} - \bar{x}^2} = \sqrt{\frac{545.5}{100} - 0.17^2}$

$= 2.33$ (3 s.f.).

$t = 5x + 52 \Rightarrow t = 5\bar{x} + 52$

So, $\bar{t} = (5 \times 0.17) + 52$

$= 52.85 = 52.9$ (3 s.f.)

$S_t = 5S_x = 11.64$

$= 11.6$ (3 s.f.)

First calculate the mean and S.D. of the (coded) x-values.

We now need to convert these to t-values, using the coding formula.

Note that the $+52$ does not affect the spread of the data.

(d) Because there are extreme values in the data (e.g. 30 and 98), it would be more appropriate to use the median and IQR.

Since all values are used to find the mean and S.D. extreme values will give a biased impression of the data.

(2) (a) $\bar{t_1} = \frac{\Sigma t_1}{20} = \frac{454}{20}$

$= 22.7$ s

$S_{t_1} = \sqrt{\frac{\Sigma t_1^2}{20} - \bar{t_1}^2} = \sqrt{\frac{13\,502}{20} - 22.7^2} = 12.6$ s

Here there are no frequencies.

These formulae are not in the formula booklet.

(b) $\bar{t_2} = \frac{\Sigma t_2}{24} = 22.5$ s

$\Rightarrow \Sigma t_2 = 24 \times 22.5 = 540$

$\therefore$ Mean of all 44 participants $= \frac{454 + 540}{44}$

$= 22.6$ s (3 s.f.)

$S_{t_2}^2 = \frac{\Sigma t_2^2}{24} - \bar{t_2}^2 = 72.0$

$\Rightarrow \Sigma t_2^2 = 24(72 + 22.5^2)$

$= 13\,878$

Hence, the sum of the squares for the total population

$= 13\,502 + 13\,878 = 27\,380$

$\therefore$ New S.D. $= \sqrt{\frac{27\,380}{44} - 22.6^2}$

$= 10.6$ (3 s.f.)

We first find the sum of the new data which has been introduced.

$\frac{\text{Total sum}}{\text{Total number}} = $ mean of total.

Variance $= $ S.D.^{2}

Statistics 1

(3) Width of bar representing the class $160 - 199$

$= 199.5 - 159.5 = 40$

|1.2|
159.5   199.5

$\therefore$ frequency density $= \frac{48}{40}$

$= 1.2$

Upper class boundary $-$ Lower class boundary.

For a histogram, we need the frequency density $= \dfrac{\text{frequency}}{\text{class width}}$.

So, 40 mm $\equiv$ 4 cm on the rainfall axis.

and $1.2 \equiv 18$ cm on the frequency density axis.

(a) $200 - 239$ has same width i.e. 4 cm.

frequency density $= \frac{36}{40} = 0.9$

$\therefore$ Height of bar $= \frac{0.9}{1.2} \times 18$

$= 13.5$ cm

(b) $240 - 299$ has width of 60

$\therefore$ Width of bar $= \frac{60}{40} \times 4 = 6$ cm

frequency density $= \frac{23}{60}$

$\therefore$ Height of bar $= \frac{23/60}{1.2} \times 18$

$= 5.75$ cm

4.2 Probability

(1)

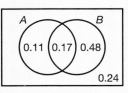

When completing the probabilities in a Venn Diagram, always work out from the middle i.e. fill in the $P(A \cap B)$ value *first*.

Once the Venn Diagram is complete all these answers can be found from it.

(a) $P(A \cap B') = 0.11$

(b) $P(B) = 0.65$

(c) $P(A' \mid B') = \frac{0.24}{0.35}$

$= 0.686$ (3 s.f.)

(d) For independence,

$P(A' \mid B') = P(A')$

but $0.686 \neq 1 - 0.28 = 0.72$

$\therefore$ Not independent.

An alternative is to check to see if $P(A \cap B) = P(A) \times P(B)$ – if not they are not independent.

(2) (a) If independent $P(E) = P(E \mid F)$

but $\frac{1}{2} \neq \frac{3}{4}$

Hence not independent.

This definition of independence is more intuitive than the one above.

(b) $P(F \mid E) = \dfrac{P(E \cap F)}{P(E)}$

$\Rightarrow \dfrac{3}{8} = \dfrac{P(E \cap F)}{\frac{1}{2}}$

$\Rightarrow P(E \cap F) = \frac{3}{16}$

(c) $P(E \mid F) = \dfrac{P(E \cap F)}{P(F)}$

$\dfrac{3}{4} = \dfrac{\frac{3}{16}}{P(F)}$

$\Rightarrow P(F) = \frac{1}{4}$

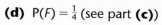

$P(F \mid E') = \dfrac{P(F \cap E')}{P(E')}$

$= \dfrac{\frac{1}{16}}{\frac{8}{16}}$

$= \frac{1}{8}$

(d) $P(F) = \frac{1}{4}$ (see part **(c)**)

(e) $P(E \mid F') = \dfrac{P(E \cap F')}{P(F')}$

$= \dfrac{\frac{5}{16}}{\frac{3}{4}}$

$= \frac{5}{12}$

> Using the other piece of information given.

> We can now complete a Venn Diagram.

> This formula needs to be familiar.

> It may be instructive to look at the tree diagrams for the events E and F:

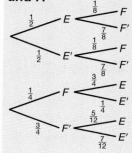

(3) (a)

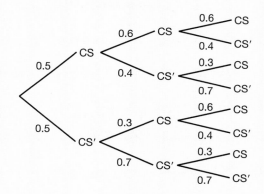

$P(CS\,CS\,CS) = 0.5 \times 0.6 \times 0.6$

$= 0.18$

(b) $P(CS'\,CS\,CS \text{ or } CS\,CS'\,CS \text{ or } CS\,CS\,CS')$

$= P(CS'\,CS\,CS) + P(CS\,CS'\,CS) + P(CS\,CS\,CS')$

$= (0.5 \times 0.3 \times 0.6) + (0.5 \times 0.4 \times 0.3) + (0.5 \times 0.6 \times 0.4)$

$= 0.09 + 0.06 + 0.12$

$= 0.27$

> CS – clean sheet.
> CS′ – not a clean sheet (i.e. goal conceded).
>
> A tree diagram is the easiest way to solve this type of problem.

> There are 3 possibilities: a goal is conceded in the 1st, 2nd or 3rd game.

(c) P(CS in 2nd game | CS in 3rd game)

$$= \frac{\text{P(CS in 2nd and 3rd games)}}{\text{P(CS in 3rd game)}}$$

$$= \frac{\text{P(CSCSCS or CS'CSCS)}}{\text{P(CSCSCS or CSCS'CS or CS'CSCS or CS'CS'CS)}}$$

$$= \frac{(0.5 \times 0.6 \times 0.6) + (0.5 \times 0.3 \times 0.6)}{(0.5 \times 0.6 \times 0.6) + (0.5 \times 0.4 \times 0.3) + (0.5 \times 0.3 \times 0.6) + (0.5 \times 0.7 \times 0.3)}$$

$$= \frac{0.18 + 0.09}{0.18 + 0.06 + 0.09 + 0.105}$$

$$= \frac{0.27}{0.435} = 0.621$$

Using $P(A \mid B) = \dfrac{P(A \cap B)}{P(B)}$.

(4) (a) Total no. of students $= 46$
$P(M \cap B) = \frac{9}{46}$

(b) $P(C \mid F) = \dfrac{P(C \cap F)}{P(F)} = \dfrac{6/46}{26/46}$

$$= \frac{6}{26} = \frac{3}{13}$$

Using the formula *or* more simply
$$\frac{6}{(8 + 12 + 6)}.$$

(c) $P(F \mid A') = \dfrac{P(F \cap A')}{P(A')} = \dfrac{18/46}{31/46} = \dfrac{18}{31}$

Using the formula *or* more simply
$$\frac{12 + 6}{(9 + 4 + 12 + 6)}.$$

(d) $P(A \text{ or } B \mid M)$

$$= \frac{7 + 9}{(7 + 9 + 4)} = \frac{16}{20} = \frac{4}{5}$$

4.3 Discrete random variables

(1) (a) $-3k - 2k - k = 1$
$\Rightarrow k = -\frac{1}{6}$
i.e. $P(X = x) = \frac{1}{6}(3 - x)$

Total probability is 1.

(b) $E(X) = (0 \times \frac{3}{6}) + (1 \times \frac{2}{6}) + (2 \times \frac{1}{6}) + (3 \times \frac{0}{6})$
$\quad = 0 + \frac{2}{6} + \frac{2}{6} + 0$
$\quad = \frac{2}{3}$

$E(X) = \Sigma P(X = x) \cdot x.$

(c) $E(3X - 2)$
$= 3E(X) - 2$
$= (3 \times \frac{2}{3}) - 2$
$= 0$

$E(aX + b) = aE(X) + b.$
This needs to be learned.

(d) $\text{Var}(3X - 2)$
$= 3^2\text{Var}(X)$
$= 9\text{Var}(X)$
$\text{Var}(X) = E(X^2) - E^2(X)$
$= (0^2 \times \frac{3}{6}) + (1^2 \times \frac{2}{6}) + (2^2 \times \frac{1}{6}) + (3^2 \times \frac{0}{6}) - (\frac{2}{3})^2$
$= \frac{2}{6} + \frac{4}{6} - \frac{4}{9} = \frac{5}{9}$
So, $\text{Var}(3X - 2) = 9 \times \frac{5}{9} = 5.$

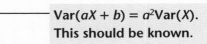

$\text{Var}(aX + b) = a^2\text{Var}(X).$
This should be known.

Alternatively: $\mathrm{Var}(3X - 2) = \mathrm{E}(3X - 2)^2 - \mathrm{E}^2(3X - 2)$

x:	0	1	2	3
$\mathrm{P}(X = x)$:	$\frac{3}{6}$	$\frac{2}{6}$	$\frac{1}{6}$	0
$3x - 2$:	-2	1	4	7
$(3x - 2)^2$:	4	1	16	49

So, $\mathrm{E}((3x - 2)^2) = (4 \times \frac{3}{6}) + (1 \times \frac{2}{6}) + (16 \times \frac{1}{6}) + (49 \times 0)$

$\qquad\qquad\qquad = 2 + \frac{1}{3} + \frac{8}{3} = 5$

So, $\mathrm{Var}(3X - 2) = 5 - 0^2 = 5$

← *This method relies on finding the probability distribution of $3X - 2$.*

← *As before.*

(2) (a) $\mathrm{E}(2X + 1) = 5$

$\Rightarrow 2\mathrm{E}(X) + 1 = 5$

$\Rightarrow \qquad \mathrm{E}(X) = 2$

← $\mathrm{E}(aX + b) = a\mathrm{E}(X) + b$
← $(\mathrm{E}(aX + b) = \mathrm{E}(aX) + \mathrm{E}(b)$
← $\qquad\qquad = a\mathrm{E}(X) + b$

(b) $\mathrm{Var}(2X + 1) = 2$

$\Rightarrow 4\mathrm{Var}(X) = 2$

$\Rightarrow \quad \mathrm{Var}(X) = \frac{1}{2}$

← $\mathrm{Var}(aX + b) = a^2\mathrm{Var}(X)$

(c) $\mathrm{Var}(X) = \mathrm{E}(X^2) - \mathrm{E}^2(X)$

$\Rightarrow \quad \frac{1}{2} = \mathrm{E}(X^2) - 2^2$

$\Rightarrow \mathrm{E}(X^2) = 4\frac{1}{2}$

(d) $\mathrm{E}(X - 2)^2$

$= \mathrm{E}(X^2 - 4X + 4)$

$= \mathrm{E}(X^2) - \mathrm{E}(4X) + \mathrm{E}(4)$

$= 4\frac{1}{2} - 4\mathrm{E}(X) + 4$

$= 4\frac{1}{2} - (4 \times 2) + 4$

$= \frac{1}{2}$

← *Multiplying out the brackets.*

(3) (a) $0.1 + 0.1 + 0.05 + 0.2 + 0.15 + 0.05 + 0.15 + a = 1$

$\Rightarrow a = 0.2$

← *Total probability is 1.*

(b) $F(3.5) = \mathrm{P}(S \leq 3.5)$

$\qquad = 0.1 + 0.1 + 0.05 = 0.25$

← *F is the cumulative probability function.*

(c) $\mathrm{P}(\,|\,S - 3\,|\, < 2)$

$= \mathrm{P}(-2 < (S - 3) < 2)$

$= \mathrm{P}(1 < S < 5)$

$= \mathrm{P}(S = 2 \text{ or } S = 3 \text{ or } S = 4)$

$= 0.1 + 0.05 + 0.2 = 0.35$

← *We need to change the modulus inequality into an easier form.*
← *Adding 3 throughout.*

(d) $\mathrm{E}(S) = (1 \times 0.1) + (2 \times 0.1) + (3 \times 0.05) + (4 \times 0.2) + (5 \times 0.15) + (6 \times 0.05) +$

$\qquad\qquad (7 \times 0.15) + (8 \times 0.2)$

$\qquad = 0.1 + 0.2 + 0.15 + 0.8 + 0.75 + 0.3 + 1.05 + 1.6$

$\qquad = 4.95$

(e) $\mathrm{Var}(S) = \mathrm{E}(S^2) - \mathrm{E}^2(S)$

$\mathrm{E}(S^2) = 29.85$

So, $\mathrm{Var}(S) = 29.85 - 4.95^2$

$\qquad\qquad = 5.3475$

← $\mathrm{E}(S^2) = \sum\limits_{\text{all }S} \mathrm{P}(S = s) \cdot S^2$

(4)

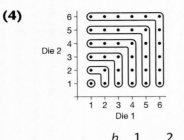

h	1	2	3	4	5	6
$P(H = h)$	$\frac{1}{36}$	$\frac{3}{36}$	$\frac{5}{36}$	$\frac{7}{36}$	$\frac{9}{36}$	$\frac{11}{36}$

(a) $H = 3$ comes from the outcomes:
(1, 3) (2, 3) (3, 3) (3, 2) (3, 1)
Hence $P(H = 3) = \frac{5}{36}$

(b) For $h = 1$:
$\frac{1}{36} = (p \times 1) + q = p + q$ ①
For $h = 2$:
$\frac{3}{36} = (p \times 2) + q = 2p + q$ ②
②−①: $\frac{2}{36} = p \Rightarrow q = -\frac{1}{36}$
i.e. $p = \frac{1}{18}$; $q = -\frac{1}{36}$
i.e. $P(H = h) = \frac{h}{18} - \frac{1}{36} = \frac{1}{36}(2h - 1)$

(c) $E(3H - 2)$
$= 3E(H) - 2$
$E(H) = \frac{1}{36} + \frac{6}{36} + \frac{15}{36} + \frac{28}{36} + \frac{45}{36} + \frac{66}{36}$
$= \frac{161}{36}$
So, $E(3H - 2) = 3 \times \frac{161}{36} - 2 = \frac{161}{12} - \frac{24}{12} = \frac{137}{12}$

> This diagram (possibility space) shows all 36 possible outcomes when the two dice are rolled.
>
> The dots are grouped for:
> $H = 1$, $H = 2$, ..., $H = 6$.
> e.g. $H = 4$ comes from the outcomes
> (1, 4) (2, 4) (3, 4) (4, 4) (4, 3) (4, 2) (4, 1).

> This is the type of explanation required.

> Set up 2 simultaneous equations.

> Check that the formula works for all the values of h.

> Use $E(aX + b) = aE(X) + b$ to simplify first.
> Now find $E(H)$.

4.4 Linear regression and correlation

(1) (a)

(b) $S_{Tt} = \Sigma Tt - \dfrac{\Sigma T \Sigma t}{6}$

$= 5953.33 - \dfrac{187.7 \times 214}{6}$

$= -741.30$

$S_{tt} = \Sigma t^2 - \dfrac{(\Sigma t)(\Sigma t)}{6}$

$= 9337.7 - \dfrac{214^2}{6} = 1705.03$

If equation of regression line of T on t is
$T = a + bt$ then

$b = \dfrac{S_{Tt}}{S_{tt}} = -\dfrac{741.30}{1705.03} = -0.43477$

$\bar{T} = a + b\bar{t}$

$\Rightarrow a = \dfrac{187.7}{6} - (-0.43477) \times \dfrac{214}{6}$

$= 46.79 \ldots = 46.8$ (3 s.f.)

So, $T = 46.8 - 0.435t$

> Although these formulae are in the formula book, it is a good idea to learn them.

> Obtain this formula by replacing T by t in the above formula.

> The 'mean point' must lie on the regression line.

(c) Intercept: 46.8 °C should be the average daily maximum temperature in August for a place on the Equator (0° latitude). Gradient: -0.435 °C per ° latitude – for every degree increase in latitude, the average daily maximum temperature in August goes down by 0.435 °C, starting on the 14°N parallel.

In practice, it may not be, since $t = 0$ is way out of the range of the data.

The data starts at $t = 14$.

(d) When $t = 9$, $T = 42.9$ °C

(e) $t = 9$ is outside the range of the data, so the regression line may not be a good predictor.

(2) (a) $r_{fc} = r_{xy} = \dfrac{S_{xy}}{\sqrt{S_{xx} S_{yy}}}$

The P.M.C.C. is unaffected by coding.

$S_{xy} = \Sigma xy - \dfrac{\Sigma x \Sigma y}{26}$

$= 51\,665.56 - \dfrac{880 \times 76.62}{26}$

$= 49\,072.26\dots$

It's a good idea to show all your working when finding S_{xy}, S_{xx} and S_{yy}.

If you make a mistake, you will receive credit for your method.

$S_{xx} = \Sigma x^2 - \dfrac{(\Sigma x)^2}{26}$

$= 1\,604\,848 - \dfrac{(880)^2}{26}$

$= 1\,575\,063.38\dots$

Final numerical answers should generally be given to 3 s.f., so you should work to at least 4 s.f. in your calculations.

$S_{yy} = \Sigma y^2 - \dfrac{(\Sigma y)^2}{26}$

$= 1867.81 - \dfrac{76.62^2}{26}$

$= 1642.016\dots$

So, $r_{fc} = \dfrac{49\,072.26\dots}{\sqrt{157\,5063.38 \times 1642.016}}$

$= 0.964\,93\dots$

$= 0.965$ (3 s.f.)

(b) Since 0.965 is high and indicates a strong correlation, this would support the calculation of a regression line of c on f.

(c) Suppose $y = a + bx$

then $b = \dfrac{S_{xy}}{S_{xx}} = \dfrac{49\,072.26}{1\,575\,063.38}$

$= 0.031\,155\,7\dots$

and $a = \bar{y} - b\bar{x} = \dfrac{76.62}{26} - 0.0311\dots \times \left(\dfrac{880}{26}\right)$

$= 1.892\,42\dots$

So, $y = 1.892\,42 + 0.031\,155\,7x$

$\Rightarrow c - 100 = 1.892\,42 + 0.031\,155\,7(f - 4500)$

$\Rightarrow c = 0.031\,155\,7f - 38.308$

i.e. $c = 0.0312f - 38.3$

i.e. $c = -38.3 + 0.0312f$

We now change the variables to c and f.

Using the coding formulae.

Giving answers to 3 s.f., produces this answer.

Statistics 1

(d) $b = 0.0312$ means that if the FTSE 100 goes up by 1 point, then c will go up by £0.0312, i.e. 3.12p.

(e) When $f = 4800$,
$c = £111$ (3 s.f.) ← Using the equation of the regression line.

(f) Probably not a good idea as it would involve extrapolation outside the range of the data.

4.5 The Normal distribution

(1) (a) Q_1 is 21st figure. ← Use $\frac{N}{4}$th as N is large ($N = 84$).
This occurs in 2nd interval.
$Q_1 = 0.5 + (\frac{13}{21} \times 0.5) = 0.81$ ← Using linear interpolation – note that 0.5 is the lower class boundary of the interval in which Q_1 lies.
Q_3 is 63rd figure.
This occurs in 4th interval.
$Q_3 = 1.5 + (\frac{11}{19} \times 0.5) = 1.79$ Use $\frac{3N}{4}$th as N is large ($N = 84$).

(b) For z the standard normal variable, $Q_1 = -0.675$ and $Q_3 = 0.675$.
So, $0.81 = \mu - 0.675\sigma$ ← Using Q_1 and Q_3 found in part **(a)** to set up 2 simultaneous equations.
$\qquad 1.79 = \mu + 0.675\sigma$

Solving, gives $\sigma = 0.726$
and $\qquad\qquad \mu = 1.3$

(c) These are quite different from the actual values so the normal probability model is a poor one.

(2) $Y \sim N(31.8, 6.7)$ ← Change this to a *cumulative probability equation*.

(a) $P(Y > y) = 0.1867$

$\Rightarrow P(Y < y) = 0.8133$ ← Standardising.

$\Rightarrow P(z < \frac{y - 31.8}{\sqrt{6.7}}) = 0.8133$ ← Reading the tables 'in reverse'.

$\Rightarrow \frac{y - 31.8}{\sqrt{6.7}} = \Phi^{-1}(0.8133) = 0.89$

$\Rightarrow y = 34.1$ (3 s.f.)

(b) $P(|Y - 31.8| < a) = 0.9356$

$P(-a < Y - 31.8 < a) = 0.9356$

$P(31.8 - a < Y < 31.8 + a) = 0.9356$

$P\left(\dfrac{-a}{\sqrt{6.7}} < z < \dfrac{a}{\sqrt{6.7}}\right) = 0.9356$

$\Phi\left(\dfrac{a}{\sqrt{6.7}}\right) - \Phi\left(\dfrac{-a}{\sqrt{6.7}}\right) = 0.9356$

$\Phi\left(\dfrac{a}{\sqrt{6.7}}\right) - \left(1 - \Phi\left(\dfrac{a}{\sqrt{6.7}}\right)\right) = 0.9356$

$\Rightarrow \qquad 2\Phi\left(\dfrac{a}{\sqrt{6.7}}\right) = 1.9356$

$\Rightarrow \qquad \Phi\left(\dfrac{a}{\sqrt{6.7}}\right) = 0.9678$

$\Rightarrow \qquad \dfrac{a}{\sqrt{6.7}} = \Phi^{-1}(0.9678) = 1.85$

$\Rightarrow \qquad a = 4.79 \text{ (3 s.f.)}$

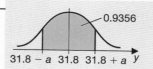

Standardising.

Using $\Phi(-t) = 1 - \Phi(z)$.

Reading the tables 'in reverse'.

(c) $P(Y < 33 \mid Y > 30)$

$= \dfrac{P(Y > 30 \cap Y < 33)}{P(Y > 30)}$

$= \dfrac{P(30 < Y < 33)}{P(Y > 30)}$

$= \dfrac{P\left(\dfrac{30 - 31.8}{\sqrt{6.7}} < z < \dfrac{33 - 31.8}{\sqrt{6.7}}\right)}{P\left(z > \dfrac{30 - 31.8}{\sqrt{6.7}}\right)}$

$= \dfrac{P(-0.70 < z < 0.46)}{P(z > -0.70)}$

$= \dfrac{\Phi(0.46) - \Phi(-0.70)}{1 - \Phi(-0.70)}$

$= \dfrac{\Phi(0.46) - (1 - \Phi(0.7))}{1 - (1 - \Phi(0.7))}$

$= \dfrac{\Phi(0.46) + \Phi(0.7) - 1}{\Phi(0.7)}$

$= \dfrac{0.6772 + 0.7580 - 1}{0.7580}$

$= 0.5741$

Using $\left(P(A \mid B) = \dfrac{P(A \cap B)}{P(B)}\right)$.

Standardising both the numerator and denominator.

Using $\Phi(-z) = 1 - \Phi(z)$ this follows from the symmetry of the graph.

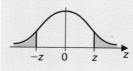

Statistics 1

Questions with model answers

C grade candidate – mark scored 7/10

Examiner's Commentary

(1) 85   76   93   38   29   67   76   58   42

(a) The numbers in the list are to be sorted into descending order. Perform a quick sort to obtain the sorted list. You must give the state of the list after each pass and indicate the pivots used. **[5]**

For help see Revise AS Study Guide section 5

35   85   93   38   **29**   67   76   58   42

35   85   93   38   **67**   76   58   42   **29**

85   **93**   76   **67**   35   **38**   58   42   **29**

93   85   76   **67**   58   42   **38**   35   **29**

List in order so stop.

The data is to be packed into bins of size 200.

(b) Calculate the lower bound on the number of bins needed. **[2]**

523 ÷ 200 = 2.615. So 3 bins needed.

(c) Use the first fit decreasing bin packing algorithm to fit the data into the bins. **[3]**

Bin 1:   93   76   29 ←

Bin 2:   85   67   42

Bin 3:   58   38   35

This list is in order, but there are some errors. The first error is in line 4 of the solution. It's all to do with how the candidate reacts to a list with an even number of terms. The first time the list is even, the candidate chose the number to the right of the middle as the pivot (67). The second time in the right hand sub-list the candidate chose the number to the left of the middle (38). This is inconsistent and a serious error. The second error is in line 5 – the list is in order, but you only know that because you are quick at sorting numbers in your head. The algorithm requires to you keep going until the sub lists are of length 1 or 0. So the candidate should have selected 85 and 42 as pivots here, **2/5 marks scored.**

Correct, and most importantly the method and working are shown clearly, **2/2 marks scored.**

Make sure you follow the algorithms consistently and precisely right to the end.

Correct, 3/3 marks scored.

GRADE BOOSTER

A grade candidate – mark scored 14/16

(2) A factory is set up to produce three types of units, X, Y, Z, and can sell them for £8, £12 and £10 respectively. Restrictions on machinery mean that the total number of Y and Z produced per day cannot exceed 30. X, Y and Z take 4 man-hours, 3 man-hours and 5 man-hours respectively, and the total number of man-hours per day available is 150.

?

For help see Revise AS Study Guide section 5

(a) Set up the objective function, if x, y and z items of each unit are to be made per day. [1]

> If P is the income from sales, then we wish to maximise the income.
> Given that the income is £8 for each X, £12 for each Y and £10 for each Z, then let there be x, y, z items of each produced per day.
> Then the income is given by $P = 8x + 12y + 10z$.

Well explained, **1/1 mark.**

(b) Explain how the constraint $y + z \leqslant 30$ is produced and find the other constraint. [3]

> Total number of units of Y and Z cannot exceed 30, so $y + z \leqslant 30$.
> The other constraint comes from the number of man-hours available which is 150.
> So the other constraint is $4x + 3y + 5z \leqslant 150$.

Again, all correct. You should aim to explain each step carefully, **3/3 marks.**

(c) Set up a simplex tableau to solve the problem. [3]

b.v.	x	y	z	r	t	Value
r	0	1	1	1	0	30
s	4	3	5	0	1	150
P	−8	−12	−10	0	0	0

All correct, **3/3 marks.**

(d) Perform two complete iterations of the simplex algorithm. Take the most negative value to indicaate the pivot column at each stage. [6]

b.v.	x	y	z	r	t	Value	Comment
y	0	1	1	1	0	30	
s	4	0	2	−3	1	60	R2 − 3R1
P	−8	0	2	12	0	360	R3 + 12R1

b.v.	x	y	z	r	t	Value	Comment
y	0	1	1	1	0	30	
x	1	0	$\frac{1}{2}$	$-\frac{3}{4}$	$\frac{1}{4}$	15	R2/4
P	0	0	6	6	2	480	R3 + 8R2

This is correct. An intermediate tableau could be used, so that two tableaux are used in each iteration, but this candidate has used only one tableau for each iteration. It is always a good idea to write down the row operations that are being done – it makes the method clear and helps prevent errors, **6/6 marks.**

(e) Suggest a solution and state whether it is optimal. [3]

> Because the bottom row has no negatives $x = 15$ and $y = 30$.
> So make 15 of X and 30 of Y.

The statement whether the solution is optimal is not given – while it may be assumed, the question asks for a specific answer. In addition, the income is not specifically given, **1/3 marks.**

Decision mathematics 1

5.1 Sorts, searches and packing

1 A school list consists of 897 names, all given in alphabetical order. Demonstrate how the binary search algorithm can be used to locate the name LING if it actually appears as number 743 in the table, giving the positions of the names which will be checked and the number of tests required. [5]

5.2 Minimum spanning tree

1 **(a)** Give a difference between Kruskal's and Prim's algorithm for finding a minimum spanning tree. [1]

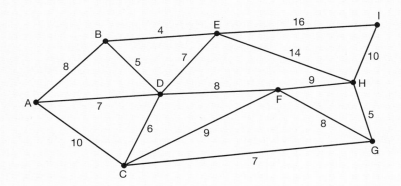

(b) Find a minimum spanning tree for the network above using

  (i) Kruskal's algorithm,

  (ii) Prim's algorithm starting at A. [3]

(c) Draw your minimum spanning tree and state its length. [2]

(d) State, with a reason, which algorithm is preferable for a large network. [2]

5.3 Planarity

1

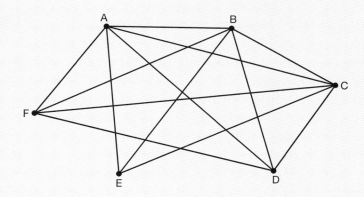

A Hamiltonian cycle for the graph above begins A, D, C, E …

(a) Complete this Hamiltonian cycle. [2]

(b) Hence use the planarity algorithm to show that the graph can not be drawn in planar form. Make your reasoning clear. [4]

One edge (not in the Hamiltonian cycle) is now removed so that the resulting graph is planar.

(c) State which edge could be removed, remove it, and show that the graph can now be drawn in planar form. [3]

5.4 Route inspection (Chinese postperson)

1

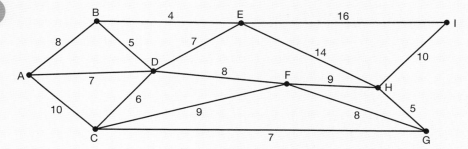

The diagram shows the lengths, in tens of metres, of some paths in a theme park. The paths need to be inspected for frost damage after winter. An inspector must walk along each path, starting and finishing at A. The inspector wishes to minimise the distance walked.

(a) Use the route inspection algorithm, starting at A, to find a route of minimal distance. You must make your method clear. [7]

(b) State the length of your route. [2]

It is now permitted to start and finish the inspection at two different vertices.

(c) State the start and finish vertices that should be chosen to minimise the total distance now walked.

Give a reason for your answer and state the length of your new route. [3]

Answers on pages 82–87 Answers on pages 82–87 Answers on pages 82–87

5.5 Matchings

1

Name	Tasks
Graham	1, 2, 4
Harry	5, 6
Jane	2, 3
Kerry	5, 6
Li	2
Max	1, 3, 6

Six workers Graham, Harry, Jane, Kerry, Li and Max are to be matched to six tasks 1, 2, 3, 4, 5 and 6. The table indicates the tasks each person is prepared to do.

(a) Draw a bipartite graph to model this situation. [1]

Initially Graham, Harry, Jane and Kerry are matched to tasks 1, 5, 2 and 6 respectively.

(b) Indicate this initial matching clearly on your bipartite graph. [1]

(c) Starting from this initial matching, use the maximum matching algorithm to find a complete matching. Indicate clearly how the algorithm has been applied, listing any alternating paths used. [5]

(d) Max now insists on doing task 6. Explain why a complete matching is no longer possible. [2]

5.6 Critical path analysis

1

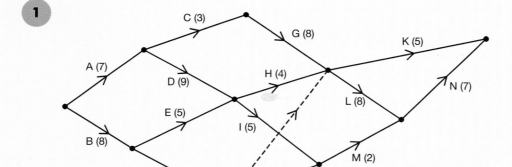

The diagram above shows an activity network for producing a holiday brochure.

(a) Find the early and late event times. [4]

(b) Write down the critical activities. [2]

(c) Calculate the total float on activity C. [1]

(d) Draw a cascade (Gantt) chart for the network. [4]

Given that each task requires only one person.

(e) State the minimum number of workers that will be needed to complete the brochure in the shortest time. Give a reason for your answer. [3]

(f) Schedule the activities using the minimum number of workers so that the brochure is produced in the shortest time. [4]

5.7 Network flows

1

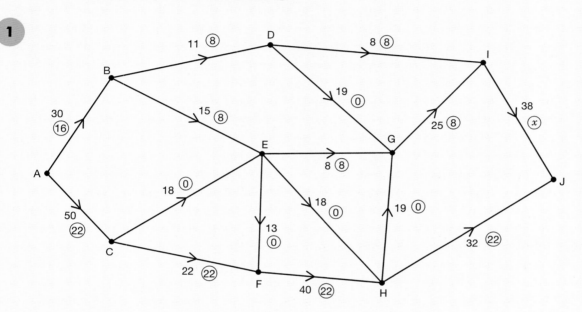

The diagram shows a capacitated directed network. The number on each arc is the capacity of the maximum flow along that arc.

The numbers in circles show a feasible flow of value 38 from A to J.

(a) State the value of x. [1]

(b) Use the labelling procedure to find the maximum flow from A to J through the network. You must list the flow-augmenting route you use together with its flow. [7]

(c) Draw a diagram to show your maximal flow pattern, and state the value of your flow. [3]

(d) Prove that your flow is maximal. [2]

Answers

5.1 Sorts, searches and packing

examiner's tips

(1) The middle name is at [1 + 897] ÷ 2 = 449.
This is before Ling so discard the pivot and all numbers before it.
The middle of the remaining list is at [450 + 879] ÷ 2 = 665 (rounding up).
This is before Ling so discard the pivot and all numbers before it.
The middle of the remaining list is at [666 + 879] ÷ 2 = 773 (rounding up).
This is after Ling so discard the pivot and all numbers after it.
The middle of the remaining list is at [666 + 772] ÷ 2 = 719.
This is before Ling so discard the pivot and all numbers before it.
The middle of the remaining list is at [720 + 772] ÷ 2 = 746.
This is after Ling so discard the pivot and all numbers after it.
The middle of the remaining list is at [720 + 745] ÷ 2 = 733 (rounding up).
This is after Ling so discard the pivot and all numbers after it.
The middle of the remaining list is at [734 + 745] ÷ 2 = 740 (rounding up).
This is after Ling so discard the pivot and all numbers after it.
The middle of the remaining list is at [741 + 745] ÷ 2 = 743.
This is Ling.
The name is found after 8 iterations.

> Do remember to discard the pivot each time and state which half of the list is being rejected. Do write down the calculations that you are doing, it will help prevent errors and make your method clear to the examiner.

5.2 Minimum spanning tree

(1) (a) For example any one of the following:
Kruskal starts by selecting the shortest arc, Prim starts at any vertex.
When using Kruskal it is necessary to check for cycles.
This does not have to be done when using Prim.
Prim's tree 'grows' in a connected fashion, Kruskal's tree may not be connected until the end.

> A lot of candidates simply list Prim's then Kruskal's algorithm and leave it to the examiner to 'spot the difference'. This may result in mark loss. If you are asked to find a difference between two algorithms **you** need to identify a feature that is different about them.
> (You also need to remember which name goes with which algorithm!)
> There are many other correct statements too.

(b) (i) BE, {BD, HG}, DC, {AD, CG, reject DE}, {DF or FG and reject the other one, reject AB}, {reject FH, reject CF} then either {reject AC, HI} or maybe just {HI}.

> The edges in brackets like this { } may be in any order.
> Do work the algorithm carefully; there may be more than one edge with the same length and the next edge could be anywhere in the diagram. Make sure that you are not so focused on one end of the diagram that you miss a small edge on the other side.

(ii) AD, DB, BE, DC, CG, GH, DF or FG, HI.

> Some candidates think that you can only run Prim in matrix form, this is not true.
> Do work the algorithm carefully; the new vertex can join into the growing tree at any vertex, not just the last one linked. Here the first few arcs follow on and you can get swept up in the tide! Lots of candidates would miss DC here and wrongly try to find an arc from E. Make sure you are not one of them!

(c) E.g.

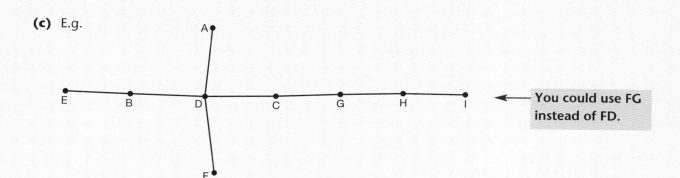

You could use FG instead of FD.

Length: 52

(d) Prim is better. In a large network it is difficult to check for cycles, which makes Kruskal's algorithm difficult to apply accurately.

Answer the question. You have to give a reason for your choice.

5.3 Planarity

(1) (a) E.g. A, D, C, E, B, F, A

Do make sure you write down a **cycle** it must finish with the same letter that it started with. A Hamiltonian cycle must include each node.

(b) Redrawing the graph with the Hamiltonian cycle as a polygon
E.g.

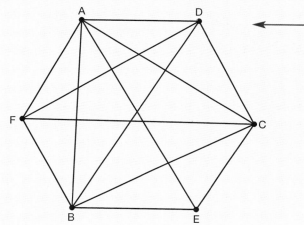

The diagram **has** to be redrawn with the Hamiltonian cycle as a polygon. It needs to be done carefully so that you don't miss out any edges (or introduce any new ones!), but it never takes as long as you fear it will!

AE, DB and FC all cross each other. Although the algorithm will enable us to separate two of them the third will cross one of them. Thus the graph is not planar.

(c) E.g. remove BD, the graph may now be drawn in a planar form.

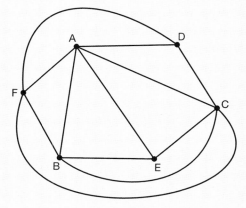

The best way to demonstrate that the graph can be drawn in planar form is to draw it!

5.4 Route inspection (Chinese postperson)

(1) (a) Odd nodes are A, B, D and G

Possible pairings are:

AB + DG = 8 + 13 = 21

AD + BG = 7 + 21 = 28

AG + BD = 17 + 5 = 22

Choose to repeat AB, DC and CF.

A possible route is:
ABEDBADCFGCGHIEHFDCA

> You must list all possible pairs of matching – If there are four odd nodes there will be three pairings that need to be tested.
> The shortest route from D to G is DCG.
> The shortest route from B to G is BDCG.
> The shortest route from A to G is ACG.
> Always make it clear which paths you are repeating and always make sure that you use paths that are on the diagram! DG does not exist on the diagram, so we must repeat DF and FG, as well as AB.
> A gobbledegook word is sufficient to make your route clear.

(b) 133 + 21 = 154

> It is worth showing your working here, as weight of network + weight of repeated arcs. If you make an error calculating the weight of the network, you may still be eligible for a method mark. If you make the same error but just write down the wrong answer you are unlikely to get any marks.

Length of route is 1540 m

(c) BD is the smallest path between two odd vertices so we wish to keep this. We therefore want to eliminate AG as a repeated route, so start at A and finish at G (or vice versa).

The length of the new route is 133 + 5 = 138 m
so 1380 m

> Do check units – it was way back in line 1 of the question that the units were mentioned. It is worth rereading the question at the end to check any units.

> You are asked to give a reason, so make your thinking clear.
> You are not asked to list the new route – just to state its length.

5.5 Matchings

(1) (a) and **(b)**

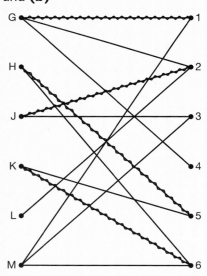

> Draw lines with a ruler and make your initial matching distinctive. It is worth double checking this first diagram since all the rest of the work will depend upon it.

> Since there are two unmatched vertices it will be necessary to use two alternating paths to obtain a complete matching. Each alternating path must start at an unmatched vertex and finish at an unmatched vertex. Don't forget the change status step and always make the final (complete) matching clear.

(c) E.g. Alternating paths L − 2 = J − 3 and M − 1 = G − 4
Changing status gives L = 2 − J = 3 and M = 1 − G = 4
Giving the complete matching
G = 4, H = 5, J = 3, K = 6, L = 2, M = 1

(d) If Max does task 6, this leaves both Harry and Kerry with only task 5. Both these workers cannot do the same task so one cannot be matched.

Think before you start writing; make your explanation clear and to the point.

5.6 Critical Path analysis

(1) (a)

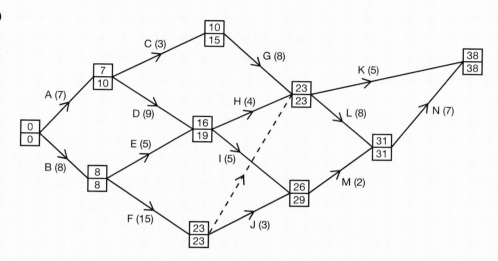

(b) Critical activities are B, F L and N.

Don't be fooled by activity K; L and N are critical but K is not.

(c) Total float on C = 15 − 7 − 3 = 5

The formula is:
Total float = late finish time − early start time − duration.

(d)

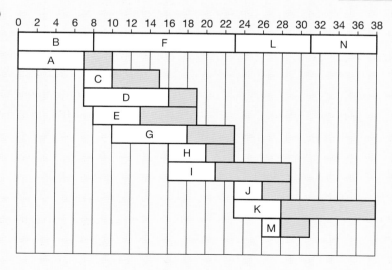

Do make sure that you show clearly the duration of each activity as well as the total float.

(e) 3 workers required

Either at time 15 activities F, D and G must be ⟵ happening.

Or $89/38 = 2.34$ and therefore 3 workers will be required.

Either one of these two methods would be acceptable – both lead to the same conclusion. Do make your working clear, stating the time and the concurrent activities in the first case, or the activity total, the time and the result of the division.

(f)

0 2 4 6 8 10 12 14 16 18 20 22 24 26 28 30 32 34 36 38

B | F | L | N
A | C | E | G | J | K
D | H | I | M

If the time is to be minimised put in the critical activities first. Do check the duration of each activity is correct and that the precedences are obeyed.

5.7 Network flows

(1) (a) $x = 16$

(b)

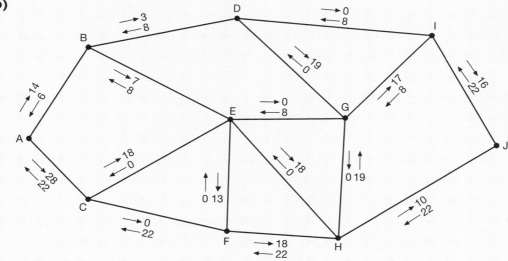

The flow can be increased by 27. A possible set of flow-augmenting routes are:
ABDGIJ – 3, ABEHJ – 7,
ACEHGIJ – 11, ACEFHJ – 3,
ACEFHGIJ – 3

> The diagram must be clear. There should be two arrows and two numbers on each arc. The examiners will need to be able to read the initial numbers that you write down to give full credit.
> There are many other ways of building the maximum flow. Make sure your routes and flows are clear.

(c)

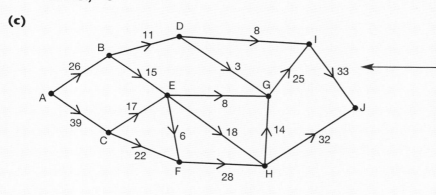

Maximum flow is 65

> It is a good idea to put the arrows onto your diagram first so that you don't forget them and so that you get them in the right direction. Make sure your diagram is consistent – the flow in at every vertex should equal the flow out and the flow leaving A should equal the flow arriving at J.

(d) Using the Maximum flow – Minimum cut theorem, the flow is 65 and a cut through DI, GI and HJ has value 65. Thus the flow is maximal.

> Do state the theorem – you must make clear the link between the flow and the cut. Make your minimum cut clear. The cut will always pass through saturated arcs.

A2 Mock Exam 1

Centre number _____

Candidate number _____

Surname and initials _____

Examining Group

Maths Core 3

Time: 1 hour 30 minutes   Maximum marks: 75

Instructions
Answer **all** questions in the spaces provided. Show all steps in your working.
The marks allocated for each question are shown in brackets.

Grading
Boundary for A grade   60/75
Boundary for C grade   45/75

N.B. Calculators should NOT be used.

1   The function f is defined by

$$f: x \rightarrow |x - 4| - 2, x \in \mathbb{R}.$$

   (a) Solve the equation $f(x) = 1$.   [3]

      The function g is defined by

$$g: x \rightarrow x^2 - 6x - 1, x \in \mathbb{R}, x \geq 0.$$

   (b) Find the range of g.   [3]

   (c) Find $gf(-1)$.   [2]

2 $f(x) = x^3 - 3x - 1$

   (a) Show that there is a root, α, of the equation $f(x) = 0$ in the interval $[1, 2]$.   [2]
      The root α is to be estimated using the iterative formula

$$x_{n+1} = \sqrt{\left(3 + \frac{1}{x_n}\right)}, \quad x_0 = 2.$$

   (b) Calculate the values of x_1, x_2, x_3 and x_4, giving your answers to 4 significant figures.   [3]

   (c) Prove that, to 5 significant figures, α is 1.8794.   [3]

3   **(a)** Using the identity for $\cos(A + B)$, prove that

$$\cos\theta \equiv 2\cos^2{\tfrac{1}{2}}\theta - 1.$$ [3]

   (b) Prove that $1 + \sin2\theta + \cos2\theta = 2\cos\theta(\sin\theta + \cos\theta)$.   [3]

   (c) Hence, or otherwise, solve the equation

$$\sin2\theta + \cos2\theta = -1, \quad 0 \leq \theta < 360°$$ [4]

4 $f(x) = \dfrac{5}{x^2 + x - 6} - \dfrac{1}{x^2 + 5x + 6}$

(a) Show that $f(x) = \dfrac{4}{x^2 - 4}$. [5]

(b) Hence find $f'(x)$. [2]

(c) Solve the equation $3f(x) - 1 = 0$. [3]

5

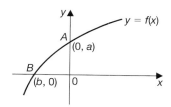

The diagram shows part of the curve with equation $y = f(x)$, $x \in \mathbb{R}$. The curve meets the y-axis at $A\,(0, a)$ and meets the x-axis at $B(b, 0)$.

(a) On separate diagrams, sketch the curve with equation

  (i) $y = f(|\,x\,|)$,

  (ii) $y = f(x - b)$.

  In each case, give the coordinates of the points at which the curve meets the axes. [4]

Given that $f(x) = 2\ln(3x + 2)$

(b) state the exact value of a, [1]

(c) find the value of b, [2]

(d) find an equation for the normal to the curve at B. [5]

6 The speed, $V\,\text{m s}^{-1}$, of a falling body is related to the time (t seconds) for which it has been falling. The relationship is given by

$$V = 200 - 200e^{-2t}, \ t \geq 0.$$

(a) Find the initial speed of the body. [1]

(b) Explain why the speed of the body is always less than $200\,\text{m s}^{-1}$. [1]

(c) Sketch the graph of V against t. [2]

(d) Find the value, to 2 significant figures, of t at the instant when $V = 180$. [4]

(e) Find $\dfrac{\text{d}V}{\text{d}t}$ in terms of V. [3]

(f) Hence find the speed of the body when its speed is increasing at a rate of $4\,\text{m s}^{-2}$. [2]

7 **(a)** Given that $y = \ln(\sec x + \tan x)$, find the exact value of $\dfrac{\text{d}y}{\text{d}x}$ at $x = \dfrac{\pi}{4}$. [5]

(b) Given that $y = e^{2x}\cos 2x$, show that

$$\frac{\text{d}y}{\text{d}x} = 2\sqrt{2}e^{2x}\cos\left(2x + \frac{\pi}{4}\right).$$ [7]

(c) Deduce an expression for $\dfrac{\text{d}^2y}{\text{d}x^2}$. [2]

A2 Mock Exam 2

Centre number _____

Candidate number _____

Surname and initials _____

Examining Group

Maths Core 4

Time: 1 hour 30 minutes   Maximum marks: 75

Instructions
Answer **all** questions in the spaces provided. Show all steps in your working.
The marks allocated for each question are shown in brackets.

Grading
Boundary for A grade   60/75
Boundary for C grade   45/75

---

1 Use the binomial theorem to expand $(4 - 2x)^{-\frac{1}{2}}$, in ascending powers of x, up to and including
the term in x^2. Give each coefficient as a simplified fraction.   [4]

2 The curve C has equation

$$xy(x + 2y) = 4.$$

Find $\dfrac{dy}{dx}$ in terms of x and y.   [6]

3 The vector equations of two straight lines are

$r = 8\mathbf{i} + 9\mathbf{j} + s(4\mathbf{i} + 2\mathbf{j} + 5\mathbf{k})$ and
$r = (-2\mathbf{i} + 5\mathbf{j} - 11\mathbf{k}) + t(3\mathbf{i} + \mathbf{j} + 3\mathbf{k})$.

(a) Find the position vector of the point of intersection of the two lines.   [5]

(b) Find the acute angle between the two lines.   [4]

4 (a) Use the substitution $x = 2\sin\theta$ to show that

$$\int_0^2 \sqrt{4 - x^2}\, dx = \pi.$$ [7]

(b) Sketch the curve with equation

$$y = \sqrt{4 - x^2} \text{ for } 0 \le x \le 2.$$ [2]

(c) Deduce the value of $\displaystyle\int_0^2 \sqrt{4 - x^2}\, dx$.   [2]

5 A curve C has parametric equations

$$x = 2\sec t, \; y = 3\tan t$$

(a) Find the Cartesian equation of C. [3]

(b) Find the gradient of C of the point where $t = \dfrac{\pi}{6}$. [4]

(c) Find an equation of the normal to the curve of the point where $t = \dfrac{\pi}{4}$. [4]

6 Given that

$$\frac{7x^2 - 12x - 1}{(2x + 1)(x - 1)^2} \equiv \frac{P}{2x + 1} + \frac{Q}{x - 1} + \frac{R}{(x - 1)^2},$$

(a) find the values of P, Q and R. [4]

(b) Hence evaluate exactly

$$\int_2^5 \frac{7x^2 - 12x - 1}{(2x + 1)(x - 1)^2} \, dx.$$ [7]

7 A curve is given by

$$x = 3\cos t, \; y = 4\sin t, \; 0 \leq t < 2\pi.$$

Find the area of the finite region bounded by the curve and the positive x- and y-axes. [11]

8 A hollow cone of base radius a and height $3a$ is held vertex downwards, as shown in the diagram.

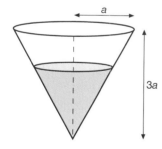

The cone is initially empty. Water is pumped into it at a rate of $4\pi \, \text{cm}^3 \, \text{s}^{-1}$.

(a) Show that, when the depth of the water in the cone is x, the volume, V, of water in the cone is given by $V = \dfrac{\pi x^3}{27}$. [3]

(b) Find the depth of the water in the cone after 16 seconds. [3]

(c) Find the rate at which the water level is rising after 16 seconds. [6]

A2 Mock Exam 1 Answers

Method (M) marks for 'knowing a method and attempting to apply it'.

Accuracy (A) marks can only be awarded if the relevant (M) mark(s) have been earned.

(B) marks are independent of method marks.

(1) (a) $|x - 4| - 2 = 1$

$\quad\ |x - 4|\quad = 3$

$\quad\ x - 4 = 3$ or $4 - x = 3$ M1

$\quad\quad\ x = 7$ or $x = 1$ A1 A1

(b) $g(x) = (x - 3)^2 - 10$ M1

minimum point at $(3, -10)$ A1

range is $g(x) \geq -10$ A1

(c) $gf(-1) = g(3) = -10$ M1 A1

(2) (a) $f(1) = -3$; $f(2) = 1$; since f is continuous   M1

change of sign $\Rightarrow \alpha \in [1, 2]$ A1

(b) $x_1 = 1.871$; $x_2 = 1.880$; $x_3 = 1.879$; $x_4 = 1.879$ B3

(c) $f(1.879\ 35) = -2.67 \ldots \times 10^{-4}$

$f(1.879\ 45) = 4.91 \ldots \times 10^{-4}$ M1 A1

Change of sign $\Rightarrow 1.879\ 35 < \alpha < 1.879\ 45$

$\Rightarrow \alpha = 1.8794$ (5 s.f.)   A1

(3) (a) $\cos(A + A) = \cos^2 A - \sin^2 A$ M1

$\cos 2A = \cos^2 A - (1 - \cos^2 A)$ M1

i.e. $\cos 2A = 2\cos^2 A - 1$

Let $A = \tfrac{1}{2}\theta$: $\cos\theta = 2\cos^2 \tfrac{1}{2}\theta - 1$ A1

(b) $1 + \sin 2\theta + \cos 2\theta$

$= \sin 2\theta + 1 + \cos 2\theta$

$= 2\sin\theta\cos\theta + 2\cos^2\theta$ M1 M1

$= 2\cos\theta(\sin\theta + \cos\theta)$ A1

(c) $\sin 2\theta + \cos 2\theta = -1$

$\Rightarrow \sin 2\theta + \cos 2\theta + 1 = 0$

$\Rightarrow 2\cos\theta(\sin\theta + \cos\theta) = 0$ M1

$\Rightarrow \cos\theta = 0$ or $\sin\theta + \cos\theta = 0$ A1

$\cos\theta = 0$ or $\tan\theta = -1$

$\theta = 90°, 270°$ or $\theta = 135°, 315°$ A1 A1

(4) (a) $f(x) = \dfrac{5}{(x + 3)(x - 2)} - \dfrac{1}{(x + 3)(x + 2)}$ M1

$= \dfrac{5(x + 2) - (x - 2)}{(x + 3)(x - 2)(x + 2)}$ M1 A1

$= \dfrac{4x + 12}{(x + 3)(x - 2)(x + 2)} = \dfrac{4(x + 3)}{(x + 3)(x - 2)(x + 2)}$ M1

$= \dfrac{4}{x^2 - 4}$ A1

(b) $f(x) = 4(x^2 - 4)^{-1}$

$f'(x) = -8x(x^2 - 4)^{-2}$ **M1 A1**

(c) $3 \cdot \left(\dfrac{4}{x^2 - 4} \right) - 1 = 0$ **M1**

$\Rightarrow x^2 - 4 = 12$

$\Rightarrow x^2 = 16$

$\Rightarrow x = \pm 4$ **A1 A1**

(5)(a) (i)

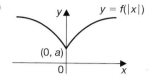

         (graph)   **B1**

         (point)   **B1**

(ii)

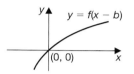

         (graph)   **B1**

         (point)   **B1**

(b) $a = f(0) = 2\ln 2$ **B1**

(c) $0 = f(b) = 2\ln(3b + 2)$ **M1**

$\Rightarrow \quad 1 = 3b + 2$ **A1**

$\Rightarrow \quad -\frac{1}{3} = b$ **A1**

(d) $f(x) = 2\ln(3x + 2)$

$f'(x) = \dfrac{6}{3x + 2}$ **B1**

$f'(-\frac{1}{3}) = \frac{6}{1} = 6$ **M1**

Gradient of normal is $-\frac{1}{6}$ **M1**

Equation of normal is $y - 0 = -\dfrac{1}{6}(x - -\dfrac{1}{3})$ **M1**

$$y = -\dfrac{x}{6} - \dfrac{1}{18}$$ **A1**

(6)(a) Put $t = 0$, $V = 200 - 200 = 0$ **B1**

(b) Since $e^{-2t} > 0$ for all t, $V < 200$ **M1**

(c)

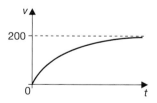

         (slope)   **B1**

         (asymptote)   **B1**

(d) $180 = 200 - 200e^{-2t}$ **M1**

$200e^{-2t} = 20$

$e^{-2t} = 0.1$ **M1**

$e^{2t} = 10$

$2t = \ln 10$ **M1**

$t = \frac{1}{2}\ln 10 = 1.2$ (2 s.f.)   **A1**

(e) $\dfrac{dV}{dt} = 400e^{-2t}$ **M1 A1**

$= 2(200 - V) = 400 - 2V$ **A1**

(f) $4 = 400 - 2V$ **M1**

$V = 198$ **A1**

(7) (a) $y = \ln(\sec x + \tan x)$

$\dfrac{dy}{dx} = \dfrac{1}{(\sec x + \tan x)} \times (\sec x\tan x + \sec^2 x)$ **M1 A1 A1**

$= \sec x \dfrac{(\tan x + \sec x)}{(\sec x + \tan x)}$

$= \sec x$ **A1**

$x = \dfrac{\pi}{4}: \dfrac{dy}{dx} = \sqrt{2}$ **A1**

(b) $y = e^{2x}\cos 2x$

$\dfrac{dy}{dx} = 2e^{2x}\cos 2x + e^{2x}(-2\sin 2x)$ **M1 A1 A1**

$= 2e^{2x}(\cos 2x - \sin 2x)$

Let $\cos 2x - \sin 2x = R\cos(2x + \alpha)$ **M1**

$R = \sqrt{2}; \alpha = \dfrac{\pi}{4}$ **M1 A1 A1**

So, $\dfrac{dy}{dx} = 2\sqrt{2}e^{2x}\cos(2x + \dfrac{\pi}{4})$

(c) $\dfrac{d^2y}{dx^2} = 4(\sqrt{2})e^{2x}\cos(2x + \dfrac{\pi}{4} + \dfrac{\pi}{4})$ **M1**

$= 8e^{2x}\cos(2x + \dfrac{\pi}{2})$ **A1**

A2 Mock Exam 2 Answers

Method (M) marks for 'knowing a method and attempting to apply it'.

Accuracy (A) marks can only be awarded if the relevant (M) mark(s) have been earned.

(B) marks are independent of method marks.

(1) $(4 - 2x)^{-\frac{1}{2}}$

$= \{4(1 + (-\tfrac{1}{2}x))\}^{-\frac{1}{2}}$

$= 4^{-\frac{1}{2}}(1 + (-\tfrac{1}{2}x))^{-\frac{1}{2}}$ **M1**

$\cong \tfrac{1}{2}(1 + (-\tfrac{1}{2})(-\tfrac{1}{2}x) + (-\tfrac{1}{2})(-\tfrac{3}{2})(-\tfrac{1}{2}x)^2)/2!$ **A2**

$= \tfrac{1}{2}(1 + \tfrac{1}{4}x + \dfrac{3x^2}{32}) = \tfrac{1}{2} + \tfrac{1}{8}x + \dfrac{3x^2}{64}$ **A1**

(2) $xy(x + 2y) = 4$

$x^2y + 2xy^2 = 4$

$x^2\dfrac{dy}{dx} + y2x + 2x2y\dfrac{dy}{dx} + y^2 . 2 = 0$ **M1 A2**

$\dfrac{dy}{dx}(x^2 + 4xy) = -2y^2 - 2xy$ **M1 A1**

$\dfrac{dy}{dx} = -2\dfrac{(y^2 + xy)}{(x^2 + 4xy)}$ **A1**

(3) (a) $8\mathbf{i} + 9\mathbf{j} + s(4\mathbf{i} + 2\mathbf{j} + 5\mathbf{k}) = (-2\mathbf{i} + 5\mathbf{j} - 11\mathbf{k}) + t(3\mathbf{i} + \mathbf{j} + 3\mathbf{k})$

$\left.\begin{array}{ll} 8 + 4s = -2 + 3t & \text{①} \\ 9 + 2s = 5 + t & \text{②} \\ 5s = -11 + 3t & \text{③} \end{array}\right\}$ **M1 A1**

solving to give $s = -1$, $t = 2$ (checking *all 3 equations*)   **M1 A1**

position vector of point is $4\mathbf{i} + 7\mathbf{j} - 5\mathbf{k}$ **A1**

(b) $(4\mathbf{i} + 2\mathbf{j} + 5\mathbf{k}) \cdot (3\mathbf{i} + \mathbf{j} + 3\mathbf{k})$

$= 29 = \sqrt{4^2 + 2^2 + 5^2} . \sqrt{3^2 + 1^2 + 3^2}\cos\theta$ **M1 A1**

$\Rightarrow \cos\theta = \dfrac{29}{\sqrt{45 \times 19}} \Rightarrow \theta = 7.35°$ **M1 A1**

(4) (a) $x = 2\sin\theta \Rightarrow \mathrm{d}x = 2\cos\theta\mathrm{d}\theta$ **B1**

$x = 0,\ 2\sin\theta = 0 \Rightarrow \theta = 0$ **B1**

$x = 2,\ 2\sin\theta = 2 \Rightarrow \theta = \dfrac{\pi}{2}$

$\displaystyle\int_0^{\frac{\pi}{2}} \sqrt{4 - 4\sin^2\theta}\ .\ 2\cos\theta\mathrm{d}\theta = 4\int_0^{\frac{\pi}{2}} \cos^2\theta\mathrm{d}\theta$ **M1 A1**

$= 4\displaystyle\int_0^{\frac{\pi}{2}} \tfrac{1}{2}(1 + \cos2\theta)\mathrm{d}\theta = 2[\theta + \tfrac{1}{2}\sin2\theta]_0^{\frac{\pi}{2}}$ **M1 A1**

$= \pi$ **A1**

(b) $y = \sqrt{4 - x^2}$

$\Rightarrow x^2 + y^2 = 4$

(shape) **B1**
(points) **B1**

(c) Area $= \dfrac{1}{4} \times \pi \times 2^2 = \pi$ **M1 A1**

(5) (a) $x = 2\sec t,\ y = 3\tan t$

$\dfrac{x}{2} = \sec t,\ \dfrac{y}{3} = \tan t$ **M1**

$\dfrac{x^2}{4} - \dfrac{y^2}{9} = 1$ **A1**

(b) $\dfrac{\mathrm{d}y}{\mathrm{d}x} = \dfrac{\mathrm{d}y}{\mathrm{d}t} \div \dfrac{\mathrm{d}x}{\mathrm{d}t}$ **M1**

$= \dfrac{3\sec^2 t}{2\sec t\tan t} = \dfrac{3}{2\sin t}$ **A1 A1**

When $t = \dfrac{\pi}{6},\ \dfrac{\mathrm{d}y}{\mathrm{d}x} = 3$ **A1**

(c) $t = \dfrac{\pi}{4},\ \dfrac{\mathrm{d}y}{\mathrm{d}x} = \dfrac{3}{\sqrt{2}}$ **M1**

$\therefore$ gradient of normal; $= \dfrac{-\sqrt{2}}{3}$ **A1**

$t = \dfrac{\pi}{4},\ x = 2\sqrt{2},\ y = 3$

$y - 3 = -\dfrac{\sqrt{2}}{3}(x - 2\sqrt{2})$ **M1**

$3y + \sqrt{2}x - 13 = 0$ **A1**

(6) (a) $7x^2 - 12x - 1 \equiv P(x-1)^2 + Q(2x+1)(x-1) + R(2x+1)$ **M1 A1**

$x = 1: \ -6 = 3R \Rightarrow R = -2$

$x = -\dfrac{1}{2}: \ \dfrac{7}{4} + 6 - 1 = \dfrac{9P}{4} \Rightarrow P = 3$ **A2**

x^2 coeff: $7 = P + 2Q \Rightarrow Q = 2$

(b) $\displaystyle\int_2^5 \left(\dfrac{3}{2x+1} + \dfrac{2}{x-1} - \dfrac{2}{(x-1)^2} \right) dx$ **M1**

$= \left[\dfrac{3}{2}\ln(2x+1) + 2\ln(x-1) + \dfrac{2}{(x-1)} \right]_2^5$ **M1 A1 A1 A1**

$= \dfrac{3}{2}(\ln 11 - \ln 5) + 2(\ln 4 - \ln 1) + 2(\dfrac{1}{4} - 1)$ **M1**

$= \dfrac{3}{2}\ln\dfrac{11}{5} + 2\ln 4 - \dfrac{3}{2}$ (or equivalent)   **A1**

(7) $x = 0 \Rightarrow 3\cos t = 0 \Rightarrow t = \pi/2 \Rightarrow y = 4$ **M1 A1**

$y = 0 \Rightarrow 4\sin t = 0 \Rightarrow t = 0 \Rightarrow x = 3$ **A1**

Area $= \displaystyle\int_{x=0}^{x=3} y\,dx = \int_{\frac{\pi}{2}}^{0} y\dfrac{dx}{dt}\cdot dt$ **M1**

$= \displaystyle\int_{\frac{\pi}{2}}^{0} 4\sin t \cdot (-3\sin t)\,dt$ **M1 A1**

$= 12\displaystyle\int_0^{\frac{\pi}{2}} -\sin^2 t\,dt$

$= 12\displaystyle\int_0^{\frac{\pi}{2}} \tfrac{1}{2}(1 - \cos 2t)\,dt$ **M1 A1**

$= 6[t - \tfrac{1}{2}\sin 2t]_0^{\pi/2}$ **A1**

$= 3\pi$ **M1 A1**

(8) (a)

$r = \dfrac{x}{3}$ **B1**

$V = \dfrac{1}{3}\pi\left(\dfrac{x}{3}\right)^2 \cdot x$ **M1**

$= \dfrac{\pi x^3}{27}$ **A1**

(b) Volume of water $= 16 \times 4\pi = 64\pi$ **B1**

$\therefore 64\pi = \dfrac{\pi x^3}{27} \Rightarrow x^3 = 64 \times 27$ **M1**

$\Rightarrow x = 4 \times 3 = 12$ **A1**

depth of water is 12 cm

(c) $V = \dfrac{\pi x^3}{27} \Rightarrow \dfrac{dV}{dx} = \dfrac{3\pi x^2}{27} = \dfrac{\pi x^2}{9}$ **M1 A1**

$\dfrac{dx}{dt} = \dfrac{dx}{dV} \times \dfrac{dV}{dt}$ **M1**

$= \dfrac{9}{\pi x^2} \times 4\pi = \dfrac{36}{x^2}$ **A1**

When $x = 12$, $\dfrac{dx}{dt} = \dfrac{36}{12^2} = \tfrac{1}{4}$ cm s^{-1} **M1 A1**